Contents

Fully endorsed by Edexcel, this *Oxford GCSE for Edexcel Foundation Revision Guide* contains all the material you need to help you prepare for your GCSE Foundation tier examination. Each topic contains:

- keypoints, examples and exercises to help you revise and fully understand the learning objectives
- past Edexcel exam questions to give you essential exam practice.

A practice exam paper is provided at the back of the book, as well as full answers to all questions.

The accompanying CD-ROM contains extra resources to aid your revision including examiners' tips and exam specification matching grids.

- The value of each digit in a number depends on its position in the number. This is called the **place value**.

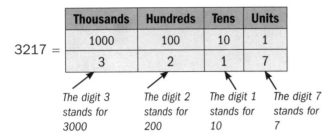

$3217 =$

Thousands	Hundreds	Tens	Units
1000	100	10	1
3	2	1	7

The digit 3 stands for 3000

The digit 2 stands for 200

The digit 1 stands for 10

The digit 7 stands for 7

- Rounding gives you the approximate size of the number.

   1446 rounded to the nearest 100 is 1400.

- A negative number is a number less than zero.

   $-3 \quad -2 \quad -1 \quad 0 \quad 1 \quad 2 \quad 3$

- An **integer** is a positive or negative whole number (including zero).

   ... ... $-3 \; -2 \; -1 \; 0 \; 1 \; 2 \; 3$ ... ... are the integers.

- A **factor** is a number that divides exactly into another number.

   1, 2, 3, 4, 6 and 12 are all factors of 12.

Factors come in pairs
$1 \times 12 = 12$
$2 \times 6 = 12$
$3 \times 4 = 12$

- Common factors are factors that are shared by two or more numbers.

   5 is a common factor of 10 and 25.

- A **prime number** is a number with exactly 2 factors.

   7 is a prime number. The only factors of 7 are 1 and 7.

1 is not a prime as it has only one factor.

- You multiply a number by an integer to get a **multiple**.

   The multiples of 3 are the same as the 3 times table:
   3 6 9 12 15 ...

- Common multiples are multiples that are shared by two or more numbers. 40 is a common multiple of 8 and 10.

$8 \times 5 = 40$
$10 \times 4 = 40$

- The Highest Common Factor (HCF) of two numbers is the largest number that is a factor of both numbers.

   The HCF of 8 and 12 is 4.

Factors of 8 : 1 2 **4** 8
Factors of 12 : 1 2 3 **4** 6 12

- The Least Common Multiple (LCM) of two numbers is the smallest number that is a multiple of both numbers.

   The LCM of 4 and 6 is 12.

Multiples of 4 : 4 8 **12** 16
Multiples of 6 : 6 **12** 18

Th	H	T	U
	3	7	6
5	2	1	7
2	5	0	0
	8	1	3
	3	2	

Example

Order these numbers from lowest to highest.

376   5217   2500   813   32

32   376   813   2500   5217

Example

Write these integers in order of size. Start with the smallest number.

0, 6, –3, 5, –8

Use a number line to help:

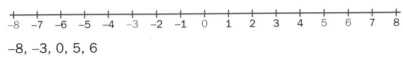

–8, –3, 0, 5, 6

Example

Round 2457 to

a the nearest 10

b the nearest 100

c the nearest 1000.

A number rounded to the nearest 10 will end with 0.

A number rounded to the nearest 100 will end with 00.

a 2457 rounded to the nearest 10 is 2460.

b 2457 rounded to the nearest 100 is 2500.

c 2457 rounded to the nearest 1000 is 2000.

Example

a Find the common factors of 18 and 24.

b Give the Highest Common Factor (HCF).

The factors of 18 are **1 2 3 6** 9 18.

The factors of 24 are **1 2 3** 4 **6** 8 12 24.

a The common factors of 18 and 24 are 1, 2, 3 and 6.

b The HCF is 6.

$1 \times 18 = 18$
$2 \times 9 = 18$
$3 \times 6 = 18$

$1 \times 24 = 24$
$2 \times 12 = 24$
$3 \times 8 = 24$
$4 \times 6 = 24$

Example

a Find the first three common multiples of 2 and 3.

b Give the Least Common Multiple (LCM).

The multiples of 2 are 2 4 **6** 8 10 **12** 14 16 **18** 20 … …

The multiples of 3 are 3 **6** 9 **12** 15 **18** 21 24 … …

a The first three common multiples of 2 and 3 are 6, 12 and 18.

b The LCM is 6.

Multiples of 2 are the 2 times table.

Multiples of 3 are the 3 times table.

Exercise N1

1 Write these numbers in figures.

   a four hundred and sixty-seven

   b fifteen thousand, two hundred and eight

   c five thousand and forty-four

   (F p2, F+ p2)

F p2 means **Oxford GCSE Maths for Edexcel Foundation Student Book** page 2.

F+ means **Foundation Plus Student Book.**

2 Give the place value of the digits in **bold**.

   a 3**8**   **b** **3**45   **c** 2**0**4   **d** 4**8**26

   (F p2, F+ p2)

Digits are the numbers.

3 Arrange the numbers 3, 4 and 5 to form six different numbers.

   Order the six numbers by size, starting with the smallest number.

   (F p2, F+ p2)

3 4 5

4 There are 199 steps from Whitby Abbey to the harbour.

   Gillian jumps down on every 4th step, and Chris jumps down on every 3rd step.

   They both start from the top of the steps.

   a List the steps that they both use.

   b How many steps do they both use?

   c Who uses the least number of steps?

   (F p10, F+ p10)

5 Here is a list of 5 numbers:

   10   11   15   18   22

   From the list, write down

   a a prime number

   b a multiple of 6

   c two factors of 60.

   d Parminda says '10 and 15 are multiples of 30.'

   He is wrong. Explain why.

   (F p10, 176, F+ p10)

6 a Write the factors of 12.

   b Write the factors of 45.

   c Find the common factors of 12 and 45.

   (F p10, F+ p10)

7 a Write the first six multiples of 10.

   b Write the first six multiples of 15.

   c Find the first two common multiples of 10 and 15.

   (F p10, F+ p10)

8 Round these numbers to the given degree of accuracy.

   a 325 (to the nearest 100)

   b 475 (to the nearest 10)

   c 4963 (to the nearest 100)

   (F p38)

9 During one day, the number of customers in a shop is 600, to the nearest 100.

   What is the lowest number of customers that could have used the shop that day?

   (F+ p38)

10 a List the factors of 28 and 42.

   b List the common factors of 28 and 42.

   c What is the Highest Common Factor (HCF) of 6 and 9?

   (F p178, F+ p10)

11 a List the first 5 multiples of 6 and 9.

   b Find the Least Common Multiple (LCM) of 6 and 9.

   (F p178, F+ p10)

12 a Write the number **seventeen thousand, two hundred and fifty-two** in figures.

   b Write the number 5367 correct to the nearest hundred.

   c Write down the value of the 4 in the number 274 863.

   (*Edexcel Ltd.*, 2005) 3 marks

13 Fiona has four cards.

   Each card has a number written on it.

   | 4 | 9 | 1 | 5 |

   Fiona puts all four cards on the table to make a number.

   a i Copy and complete the cards to show the smallest number Fiona can make with the four cards.

      ii Copy and complete the cards to show the largest number Fiona can make with the four cards.

   b Copy and complete the cards to make this true.

      Use each of Fiona's cards **once**.

   A fifth card is needed to show the result of the multiplication 4915 × 10.

   c Write the number that should be on the fifth card.

   (*Edexcel Ltd.*, 2004) 4 marks

☐ ☐ ☐ ☐

☐ ☐ ☐ ☐

☐ + ☐ = ☐ ☐

☐

Fractions, decimals and percentages

Keywords
Decimal
Equivalent
Fraction
Percentage
Recurring

- A **fraction** is a way of describing part of a whole.

  $\frac{4}{5}$ means 4 parts out of 5.

  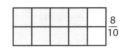 numerator

  $\frac{4}{5}$ denominator

- You can find **equivalent** fractions by multiplying or dividing the numerator and denominator by the same number.

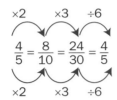

$$\frac{4}{5} = \frac{8}{10} = \frac{24}{30} = \frac{4}{5}$$

$\frac{8}{10}$

- A **decimal** is written using place values.

$96.278 =$

Tens	Units	.	Tenths	Hundredths	Thousandths
10	1	.	$\frac{1}{10}$	$\frac{1}{100}$	$\frac{1}{1000}$
9	6	.	2	7	8

The digit 9 stands for 90

The digit 6 stands for 6

The digit 2 stands for $\frac{2}{10}$

The digit 7 stands for $\frac{7}{100}$

The digit 8 stands for $\frac{8}{1000}$

- A **recurring** decimal is a decimal that repeats itself for ever.

  0.333 333 333 333 333 333 ... ... is a recurring decimal.

  $0.333\,333\,3\ldots = 0.\dot{3}$

- A **percentage** (%) is a number of parts out of 100.

  $51\% = 51$ parts out of $100 = \frac{51}{100}$

- You can find equivalents for fractions, decimals and percentages.

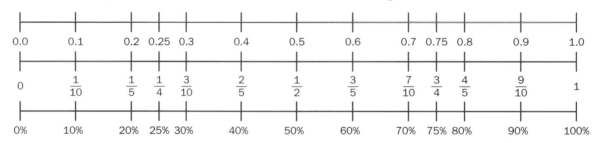

- You can order fractions, decimals and percentages using equivalents.

  0.35 $\frac{2}{5}$ 45% are in order of size, smallest first.

  $0.35 = 0.35$

  $\frac{2}{5} = 0.4$

  $45\% = 0.45$

Example

Write these numbers in order of size.

Start with the smallest number.

3.2   3.19   3.25   3.195

U .	$\frac{1}{10}$	$\frac{1}{100}$	$\frac{1}{1000}$
3 . 2			
3 . 1	9		
3 . 2	5		
3 . 1	9	5	

3.19   3.195   3.2   3.25

Example

a Change these fractions so that they have a common denominator.

$\frac{3}{8}$ $\frac{2}{5}$ $\frac{3}{10}$ $\frac{1}{4}$ $\frac{1}{2}$

b Order the fractions in size, smallest first.

a 8, 5, 10, 4, 2 are factors of 40.

$$\frac{3}{8} = \frac{15}{40} \quad \frac{2}{5} = \frac{16}{40} \quad \frac{3}{10} = \frac{12}{40} \quad \frac{1}{4} = \frac{10}{40} \quad \frac{1}{2} = \frac{20}{40}$$

(×5, ×8, ×4, ×10, ×20)

b $\frac{1}{4}$ $\frac{3}{10}$ $\frac{3}{8}$ $\frac{2}{5}$ $\frac{1}{2}$

Example

Convert each decimal to

a a percentage   **b** a cancelled fraction.

0.75   0.8   0.05

a $0.75 = \frac{75}{100} = 75\%$

$0.8 = \frac{8}{10} = \frac{80}{100} = 80\%$

$0.05 = \frac{5}{100} = 5\%$

$0.125 = \frac{125}{1000} = \frac{12.5}{100} = 12.5\%$

b $\frac{75}{100} = \frac{3}{4}$

$\frac{80}{100} = \frac{4}{5}$

$\frac{5}{100} = \frac{1}{20}$

$\frac{125}{1000} = \frac{1}{8}$

U .	$\frac{1}{10}$	$\frac{1}{100}$	$\frac{1}{1000}$
0 . 7	5		
0 . 8			
0 . 0	5		
0 . 1	2	5	

Example

Emilio claims that $\frac{4}{9}$ is larger than 43%.

Is he correct? Explain your answer.

$\frac{4}{9} = 4 \div 9 = 0.444\,444\,444\,44 \ldots \ldots \ldots = 0.\dot{4}$

$43\% = \frac{43}{100} = 43 \div 100 = 0.43$

Emilio is correct.

$$\frac{0.4444}{9\overline{)4.0000}}$$

Example

Glen was given a mental arithmetic test of 20 questions.

He got three questions wrong.

Express his mark as

a a fraction   **b** a percentage.

a $\frac{17}{20}$ **b** $\frac{17}{20} = \frac{85}{100} = 85\%$

Exercise N2

1 Copy this diagram.

   a On your diagram, shade $\frac{1}{3}$ of the shape.

   b Write the unshaded fraction in its **simplest form**.

   (F p74, F+ p74)

> With fractions, **simplest form** means cancel.

2 Give the value of the digits marked in bold.

   a 3.4**5**   **b** 5**4**.6   **c** 0.00**4**6

   (F p2, F+ p2)

3 Write these numbers in order of size. Start with the smallest.

   a 4.6   4.66   4.58   4.7

   b 30.2   30.15   30.1   30.19

   c 8.5   8.45   8.55   8.455

   (F p2, F+ p2)

4 Convert each decimal to   **i** a cancelled fraction   **ii** a percentage.

   a 0.6   **b** 0.05   **c** 0.15   **d** 0.125

   (F p78–82, F+ p80)

5 Convert each percentage to   **i** a cancelled fraction   **ii** a decimal.

   a 40%   **b** 70%   **c** 65%   **d** 48%

   (F p78–82, F+ p80)

6 Convert each fraction to   **i** a percentage   **ii** a decimal.

   a $\frac{7}{10}$ **b** $\frac{27}{50}$ **c** $\frac{3}{10}$ **d** $\frac{13}{20}$

   (F p78–82, F+ p80)

7 Copy and complete the table.

	Cancelled fraction	Decimal	Percentage
a		0.5	
b			20%
c	$\frac{3}{10}$		
d		0.75	
e			90%

(F p78, 80, F+ p80)

8 Convert these fractions to recurring decimals.

   a $\frac{2}{9}$ **b** $\frac{1}{6}$ **c** $\frac{1}{7}$

(F p78, F+ p80)

9 Sophie does a spelling test. She gets 8 words correct out of 10.

Calculate her mark as **a** a cancelled fraction **b** a percentage.

(F p80, F+ p80)

10 a Change these fractions so that they have a common denominator.

   $\frac{5}{8}$ $\frac{2}{3}$ $\frac{7}{8}$ $\frac{3}{4}$ $\frac{1}{2}$

> You need the LCM of 2, 3, 4 and 8 – see N1.

  b Order the fractions in size, smallest first.

(F p76, F+ p74)

11 Write these numbers in order of size, smallest first.

  a 43% $\frac{2}{5}$ 0.48 $\frac{22}{50}$

  b 0.9   83% $\frac{4}{5}$ 0.85

> You need to change each number to the same type, either fraction, decimal or percentage – your choice.

  c 0.17   22% $\frac{1}{4}$ $\frac{1}{5}$

(F p82, F+ p80)

12

> **Cat facts**
> - 40% of people named cats as their favourite pet.
> - 98% of women said they would rather go out with someone who liked cats.
> - About $7\frac{1}{2}$ million families have a cat.
> - $\frac{1}{4}$ of cat owners keep a cat because cats are easy to look after.

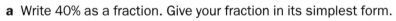

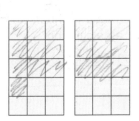

  a Write 40% as a fraction. Give your fraction in its simplest form.

  b Write 98% as a decimal.

  c Write $7\frac{1}{2}$ million in figures.

  d Write $\frac{1}{4}$ as a percentage.

  e What percentage of people did **not** name cats as their favourite pet?

(*Edexcel Ltd., 2005*) 6 marks

13 Here are two fractions: $\frac{3}{5}$ and $\frac{2}{3}$.

Explain which is the larger fraction.

You may use grids to help with your explanation.

(*Edexcel Ltd., 2003*) 3 marks

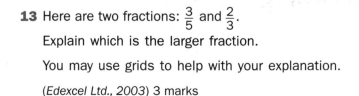

- You can use standard written methods to add, subtract, multiply and divide integers. Each method relies on **place value**.

Keywords
BIDMAS
Common denominator
Numerator
Place value
Rounded numbers

See N1 for integers.

- Adding a negative number is the same as subtracting a positive number.

$$4 + (-2) = 4 - 2$$

See N1 for negative numbers.

- Subtracting a negative number is the same as adding a positive number.

$$4 - (-2) = 4 + 2$$

- You can multiply and divide positive and negative numbers.

positive $\times$ positive = positive

positive $\times$ negative = negative

negative $\times$ positive = negative

negative $\times$ negative = positive

$$(-3) \times (-2) = +6$$

	+	−
+	+	−
−	−	+

Use the same rules for division.

- You use **BIDMAS** to decide the order of operations.

$$
\begin{aligned}
3^2 + 7 \times (8 - 5) &= 3^2 + 7 \times 3 & \text{Brackets} \\
&= 9 + 7 \times 3 & \text{Indices} \\
&= 9 + 21 & \text{Multiply} \\
&= 30 & \text{Add}
\end{aligned}
$$

Brackets
Indices or Powers
Division and
Multiplication
Addition and
Subtraction

- You add and subtract fractions using equivalent fractions with a **common denominator**.

$$\frac{3}{4} + \frac{2}{3} = \frac{9}{12} + \frac{8}{12} = \frac{17}{12} = 1\frac{5}{12}$$

See N2 for equivalent fractions.

- To multiply fractions, you multiply the **numerators** and you multiply the denominators.

$$\frac{3}{4} \times \frac{5}{8} = \frac{15}{32}$$

See N2 for numerators.

- To divide fractions, you use the relationship between multiplication and division.

$$\frac{2}{3} \div \frac{8}{9} = \frac{2}{3} \times \frac{9}{8}$$

$\div \frac{8}{9}$ is the same as $\times \frac{9}{8}$

- You use **rounded numbers** to estimate the approximate answer to a calculation.

$$\frac{47 \times 603}{295} \approx \frac{50 \times 600}{300}$$

See N1 for rounding.

$$\frac{50 \times \cancel{600}^{2}}{\cancel{300}_{1}} = \frac{100}{1}$$
$$= 100$$

Example

1648 apples are picked from an apple orchard.

They are to be stored in boxes which each hold 24 apples.

a How many boxes are needed?

b How many empty spaces will the final box have?

a $1648 \div 24$

$1648 \div 24 = \textbf{68}$ with 16 left over.

So 69 boxes are needed.

b The final box has $24 - 16 = 8$ empty spaces.

$$
\begin{array}{r}
24\overline{)1648} \\
\underline{1440} \quad 24 \times 60 \\
208 \\
\underline{192} \quad 24 \times 8 \\
16
\end{array}
$$

$24 \times 70 = 1680$
$24 \times 60 = 1440$
$24 \times 9 = 216$
$24 \times 8 = 192$

Example

Andy and Sharon work out this sum. $\dfrac{40}{5+3}$

Andy's answer is 11.

Sharon's answer is 5.

Who is correct? Give a reason for your choice.

$\dfrac{40}{5+3} = \dfrac{40}{(5+3)} = \dfrac{40}{8} = 5$ Sharon is correct.

Andy WRONGLY did
$40 \div 5 + 3 = 11$

B
I
DM
AS

Example

Calculate

a $-4 + (-6)$ **b** $-4 - (-6)$ **c** -14×-2 **d** $-14 \div 2$

a $-4 + (-6) = -4 - 6 = -10$ **b** $-4 - (-6) = -4 + 6 = +2 = 2$

c $-14 \times -2 = +28 = 28$ **d** $-14 \div 2 = -7$

Example

Calculate $3\frac{2}{5} - 2\frac{1}{4}$

$3\frac{2}{5} - 2\frac{1}{4} = 3\frac{8}{20} - 2\frac{5}{20} = 1\frac{3}{20}$

Example

Calculate

a $\dfrac{3}{4} \times \dfrac{20}{21}$ **b** $1\frac{1}{2} \times \dfrac{3}{4}$ **c** $\dfrac{4}{5}$ of 30 km

a $\dfrac{3}{4} \times \dfrac{20}{21} = \dfrac{3 \times 20}{4 \times 21} = \dfrac{60}{84} = \dfrac{5}{7}$ **b** $1\frac{1}{2} \times \dfrac{3}{4} = \dfrac{3}{2} \times \dfrac{3}{4} = \dfrac{9}{8} = 1\frac{1}{8}$

c $\dfrac{4}{5}$ of 30 km $= \dfrac{4}{5} \times \dfrac{30}{1} = \dfrac{4}{\cancel{5}_1} \times \dfrac{\cancel{30}^6}{1} = \dfrac{24}{1} = 24$ km

Example

Pat cycles 32 miles in 5 hours 20 minutes.

Calculate her speed in miles per hour.

Speed $= \dfrac{\text{Distance}}{\text{Time}} = \dfrac{32}{5\frac{1}{3}}$

$32 \div 5\frac{1}{3} = \dfrac{32}{1} \div \dfrac{16}{3} = \dfrac{32}{1} \times \dfrac{3}{16} = \dfrac{\cancel{32}^2}{1} \times \dfrac{3}{\cancel{16}_1} = \dfrac{6}{1} = 6$ mph

$20\,\text{min} = \dfrac{1}{3}$ hour

See N6 for speed.

D

T

Exercise N3

1 The readings on a gas meter are   September   38 794

                                         December   40 056

Calculate the number of units that have been used between September and December.

(F p42)

2 Work out

    a 56×14 **b** 574×35 **c** $1035 \div 23$

(F p46, F+ p46)

3 Evaluate   Evaluate means work out.

    a $-5 + (-2)$ **b** $8 - (-6)$ **c** $7 - 9$

(F p8, F+ p6)

4 Work out

    a $(-8) \times (+5)$ **b** $72 \div -9$ **c** $-54 \div -9$

(F p8, F+ p8)

5 Work out and simplify your answers if possible.   Simplify means cancel fractions down.

    a $\dfrac{3}{8} + \dfrac{7}{12}$ **b** $\dfrac{1}{4} + \dfrac{5}{12}$ **c** $1\dfrac{2}{3} - \dfrac{4}{9}$

(F p76, F+ p76)

6 Calculate and simplify if possible.

    a $\dfrac{4}{15} \times \dfrac{5}{8}$ **b** $2\dfrac{5}{8} \times 1\dfrac{1}{7}$ **c** $\dfrac{3}{8} \times 96$

(F+ p78)

7 Alex has 120 metres of rope. She cuts the rope at $\dfrac{1}{8}$ of the length.

    a Calculate $\dfrac{1}{8}$ of 120 metres.

    b How long is the remaining length of rope?

(F+ p78)

8 Calculate and simplify if possible.

    a $\dfrac{4}{9} \div \dfrac{2}{3}$ **b** $1\dfrac{1}{5} \div \dfrac{8}{15}$ **c** $8 \div \dfrac{1}{4}$

(F+ p78)

9 Estimate an approximate answer to each sum.

    a $\dfrac{290}{34}$ **b** $\dfrac{36 \times 78}{18 \times 22}$ **c** $\dfrac{49}{\frac{1}{2}}$ First round the numbers to one significant figure – see N4.

(F p38)

10 Rob uses a calculator to work out $\frac{160}{80 + 20}$.

He keeps getting an answer of 22

  a Explain what Rob is doing wrong.

  b What is the correct answer?

(F p206, F+ p206)

11 James' train journey lasts 2 hours 40 minutes.

The average speed of the train was 72 mph.

Calculate the distance of the journey.

(F+ p78)

See N6 for speed.

12 Calculate the perimeter **and** area for each shape.

State the units of your answers.

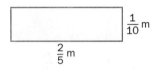 $\frac{1}{10}$ m

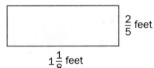 $\frac{2}{5}$ feet

 a square

$\frac{2}{5}$ m

$1\frac{1}{8}$ feet

$\frac{4}{5}$ cm

(F+ p78)

13 a Work out $\frac{11}{12} - \frac{5}{6}$.

  b Estimate the value of $\frac{68 \times 401}{198}$.

(*Edexcel Ltd., 2004*) 4 marks

14 The table shows the temperature on the surface of each of five planets.

Planet	Temperature
Venus	480 °C
Mars	−60 °C
Jupiter	−150 °C
Saturn	−180 °C
Uranus	−210 °C

  a Work out the difference in temperature between Mars and Jupiter.

  b Work out the difference in temperature between Venus and Mars.

  c Which planet has a temperature 30 °C higher than the temperature on Saturn?

The temperature on Pluto is 20 °C lower than the temperature on Uranus.

  d Work out the temperature on Pluto.

(*Edexcel Ltd., 2005*) 4 marks

Difference means subtract the two numbers.

Keywords
Appropriate degree of accuracy
Approximate
Decimal places
Estimate
Significant figures
Trial and improvement

- You need to interpret the calculator display when you are doing money calculations.

 means £8.60

means £8.06

- Some answers must be given to an **appropriate degree of accuracy**.

    £6.932 673 456 is interpreted as £6.93.

- You add and subtract decimals by putting the digits in the correct columns.

    4.1 − 0.05 = 4.05

H	T	U	.	$\frac{1}{10}$	$\frac{1}{100}$	$\frac{1}{1000}$
		4	.	1		
		0	.	0	5	

- You can round numbers to their **approximate** size using

    — **decimal places**: 3.154 rounded to 2 decimal places is 3.15.

    Allowed 2 digits after the point.

    — **significant figures**: 3.154 rounded to 2 significant figures is 3.2.

    Allowed 2 digits only.

- Using rounded numbers you can **estimate** the answer to a calculation.

    $$\frac{378}{19.8 \times 0.9} \approx \frac{400}{20 \times 1}$$

    $$\frac{\overset{20}{\cancel{400}}}{\underset{1}{\cancel{20}} \times 1} = \frac{20}{1}$$
    $$= 20$$

- You multiply decimals using the rules of multiplication and division by 10, 100, etc.

    See N8 for multiplication and division by 10, 100.

    4.5 × 38 = 45 × 38 ÷ 10

    First remove the decimal point and calculate.

    = 1710 ÷ 10

    = 171

    Then insert the decimal point in the appropriate position by dividing by 10.

    Always check your answer by approximating.

    5 × 40 = 200

- You divide by a decimal using the rules of multiplication by 10, 100, etc.

    You must divide by an integer.

    15.26 ÷ 0.7 is the same as 152.6 ÷ 7.

    Multiply both numbers by 10 or 100 until you can divide by an integer.

    152.6 ÷ 7 = 21.8

    Always check your answer by approximating.

    15 ÷ 0.5 = 30

Example

A book costs £14.75.

Calculate the cost of 35 books.

First calculate 1475 × 35

$$
\begin{array}{r}
1475 \\
35 \times \\
\hline
44250 \\
7375 \\
\hline
51625
\end{array}
$$

£14.75 × 35 = £516.25

Example

Round 43.65 to

a the nearest integer

b 1 significant figure

c 1 decimal place.

a 43.65 to the nearest integer is 44.

b 43.65 to 1 significant figure is 40.

c 43.65 to 1 decimal place is 43.7.

In example **b**, the digit 0 must be added to give 40. An answer of 4 is the wrong size. 40 is closer to 43.658 than 4.

Example

Calculate the square root of 58 by **trial and improvement**.

Give your answer to 1 decimal place.

Number	(Number)^2	
8	64	too big
7	49	too small
7.5	56.25	too small
7.6	57.76	too small
7.7	59.29	too big
7.65	58.5225	too big

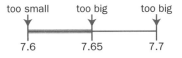

$\sqrt{58}$ = 7.6 (to 1 dp)

See N5 for square roots.

Example

Sabrina takes 1.6 hours to travel from Sheffield to Leeds.

How many minutes does her journey last?

1 hour = 60 minutes

0.6 hour = $\frac{6}{10}$ hour = $\frac{6}{10}$ × 60 minutes = $\frac{6}{10}$ × 60 = 36 minutes

See N2 and N3 for fractions.

Total time = 60 + 36 = 96 minutes

Example

If 51 × 18 = 918, calculate

a 5.1 × 18   **b** 918 ÷ 5.1

a 5 × 20 = 100   **b** 1000 ÷ 5 = 200

so 5.1 × 18 = 91.8   so 918 ÷ 5.1 = 180

15

Exercise N4

1 Sally wants to make a very large cake for a charity fete.

She needs 159 eggs.

Eggs are bought in trays of 12 eggs.

a Work out the least number of trays of eggs that Sally needs to buy. 14

b How many spare eggs will she have?

Each tray of eggs costs £1.23.

c Work out the total cost of the eggs.

(F p46, 212, F+ p46)

2 Calculate

a $6 + 3.4^2$ **b** $\dfrac{1}{0.125} - \dfrac{1}{0.5}$ **c** $\dfrac{4.6 - 3.575}{9.8 - 7.75}$

(F p214)

See N3 for BIDMAS.

3 Pat buys these items from the greengrocer.

Pat gives the greengrocer a £5 note.

How much change should she expect?

(F p210, F+ p42)

> 2 cauliflowers at 75p each
> $\frac{1}{2}$ kg of tomatoes at £1.24 a kilogram
> 3 kg of potatoes at 55p a kilogram
> 1 kg of carrots at 60p a kilogram

4 a Calculate $5.8^2 + \sqrt{34}$.

b Give your answer correct to 1 significant figure.

(F p214, 208, F+ p38)

5 Round these numbers to the required degree of accuracy.

a 18.2 to the nearest integer   **b** 3.58 to 1 decimal place

c 8.35 to 2 significant figures   **d** 18.2 to 1 significant figure

e 3.745 to 2 decimal places

(F p208, 362, F+ p38)

See N1 for integers.

6 By rounding each number to 1 significant figure, estimate

a 6.8×219 **b** 0.48×48 **c** $\dfrac{320}{98 \times 0.52}$

(F p208, F+ p38, 208)

7 The cost of a CD is £8.75.

Work out the cost of 17 of these CDs.

(F p212, F+ p46)

8 Calculate

a 16.6×4 **b** 0.3×0.3 **c** 3.4×0.6

d $4.9 \div 0.5$ **e** $9 \div 0.6$ **f** $6.72 \div 1.2$

(F p212, F+ p46)

9 Use trial and improvement to find $\sqrt{40}$ to 1 decimal place.

(F+ p170)

10 Annette starts a fitness routine.

She decides to run 4.9 km every day.

Calculate the distance she runs in

a a week

b a year.

Give your answers to an appropriate degree of accuracy.

(F+ p214)

11 Given that $56 \times 23 = 1288$, calculate

a 56×2.3

b $1288 \div 560$

(F+ p210)

12 Work out an estimate for the value of $\dfrac{378}{19.8 \times 1.9}$.

(*Edexcel Ltd., 2005*) 2 marks

See N4 for rounding to 1 significant figure.

13 Fatima bought 48 teddy bears at £9.55 each.

a Work out the amount she paid.

Fatima sold all the teddy bears for a total of £696.

She sold each teddy bear for the same price.

b Work out the price at which Fatima sold each teddy bear.

(*Edexcel Ltd., 2003*) 6 marks

14 The diagram represents a large tank in the shape of a cuboid.

The tank has a base.

It does not have a top.

The width of the tank is 2.8 metres.

The length of the tank is 3.2 metres.

The height of the tank is 4.5 metres.

The outside of the tank is going to be painted.

1 litre of paint will cover 2.5 m² of the tank.

The cost of the paint is £2.99 per litre.

Calculate the cost of the paint needed to paint the outside of the tank.

(*Edexcel Ltd., 2003*) 5 marks

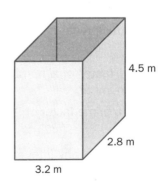

4.5 m

2.8 m

3.2 m

Keywords
Cube root
Highest Common Factor
Index
Least Common Multiple
Power
Reciprocal
Square root

- The **power** or **index** of a number tells you how many times the number must be multiplied by itself.

   $10^4 = 10 \times 10 \times 10 \times 10 = 10\,000$

- A square number is the result of multiplying an integer by itself.

   $7^2 = 7 \times 7 = 49$, so 49 is a square number.

- A cube number is the result of multiplying an integer by itself and then by itself again.

   $6^3 = 6 \times 6 \times 6 = 216$, so 216 is a cube number.

- The **square root** of a number multiplied by itself makes the number.

   $6 \times 6 = 36$, so 6 is the square root of 36.

   $\sqrt{}$ means square root. $\sqrt{36} = 6$

- A positive number has both a positive square root and a negative square root.

   The square root of 16 is 4 and −4.

   $4 \times 4 = 16$
   $-4 \times -4 = 16$
   See N3.

- The **cube root** of a number multiplied by itself and then by itself again makes the number.

   $5 \times 5 \times 5 = 125$, so 5 is the cube root of 125.

   $\sqrt[3]{}$ means cube root.
   $\sqrt[3]{125} = 5$

- When you multiply powers of the same number, you add the indices.

   $4^2 \times 4^3 = 4^{2+3} = 4^5$

   See A2 for indices in algebra.

- When you divide powers of the same number, you subtract the indices.

   $2^5 \div 2^2 = 2^{5-2} = 2^3$

- The **reciprocal** of a number is 1 divided by that number.

   The reciprocal of 4 is $\frac{1}{4}$.

   $4 \times \frac{1}{4} = 1$

- A prime factor of a number is a prime number and also a factor of the number.

   5 is a prime factor of 20, as 5 is a prime number and $5 \times 4 = 20$.

- You can write any integer as the product of its prime factors.

   $18 = 2 \times 9 = 2 \times 3 \times 3$ or $18 = 2^1 \times 3^2$

   $2^1 = 2$

- The **Highest Common Factor (HCF)** of two numbers is the largest number that is a factor of them both.

   The HCF of 9 and 12 is 3.

- The **Least Common Multiple (LCM)** of two numbers is the smallest number that is a multiple of them both.

   The LCM of 6 and 9 is 18.

Example

Sunita thinks of a number. She multiplies the number by itself.

Her answer is 121.

What number did Sunita first think of?

The square root of 121 is 11 and so Sunita's number is 11.

$\sqrt{121} = 11$
$11 \times 11 = 121$

Example

Which is larger, 2^3 or 3^2?

$2^3 = 2 \times 2 \times 2 = 8$

$3^2 = 3 \times 3 = 9$

and so 3^2 is larger than 2^3.

Example

Write 20 as the product of prime factors.

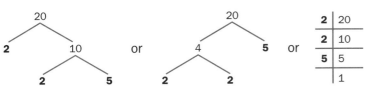

or

$\begin{array}{c|c} 2 & 20 \\ \hline 2 & 10 \\ \hline 5 & 5 \\ \hline & 1 \end{array}$

Check:
$2 \times 2 = 4$
$4 \times 5 = 20$

$20 = 2 \times 2 \times 5$

Example

Show that the square root of 21 is between 4 and 5.

$4 \times 4 = 16$

$5 \times 5 = 25$

So $\sqrt{21}$ is between 4 and 5.

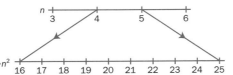

Example

a Find the Highest Common Factor (HCF) of 24 and 40.

b Find the Least Common Multiple (LCM) of 20 and 25.

a $24 = \mathbf{2 \times 2 \times 2} \times 3$

$40 = \mathbf{2 \times 2 \times 2} \times 5$

HCF is $\mathbf{2 \times 2 \times 2} = 8$

b $20 = 2 \times 2 \times \mathbf{5}$

$25 = 5 \times \mathbf{5}$

LCM is $\mathbf{5} \times 2 \times 2 \times 5 = 100$

HCF – Pick out the common factors and multiply together.

LCM – Calculate the HCF and multiply by the remaining factors.

19

Exercise N5

1 The diagrams for the square numbers 1 and 4 are shown.

Draw similar diagrams for 9 and 16.

(F p170, F+ p170)

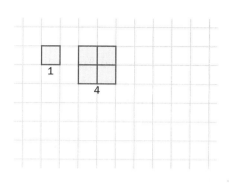

2

    a Calculate the value of each card.

    b Put the cards in order, smallest first.

    (F p174, F+ p28)

 3 Find the largest cube number below 100 000.

    (F p170, F+ p172)

4 Ben thinks of a number.

He multiplies it by itself.

His answer is 81.

    a What number did Ben first think of?

    b Write 81 using index notation.

    c Rewrite 81 in a different way using index notation.

    (F p170, 174, F+ p28, 172)

5 Find   **a** the square root   **b** the cube root of

    i 64   **ii** 1   **iii** 1 000 000

    (F p172, F+ p170)

6 Some prime numbers can be written as the sum of two square numbers.

For example, $2^2 + 3^2 = 4 + 9 = 13$

Find square numbers which sum to

    a 17   **b** 29   **c** 41   **d** 113

    (F p170, F+ p170)

See N1 for prime numbers.

7 A cube has a volume of 216 cm^3.

Calculate the length of one of its sides.

State the units of your answer.

(F p172, F+ p172)

See S4 for volume.

8 Work out the value of each of these expressions.

  a $2^3 \times 5$ **b** $5^2 \times 2^3$ **c** $3^2 \times 2^4$ **d** $6^2 \times 5^2$

  (F p174, F+ p28)

9 Calculate the reciprocal of

  a 2   **c** 25   **d** 50

  (F+ p174)

10 Calculate each value, leaving your answer in index form.

  a $10^2 \times 10^3$ **b** $10^6 \div 10^2$ **c** $10^4 \times 10^3$ **d** $\sqrt{10^2}$

  (F+ p174)

11 The cube root of 24 is between two consecutive integers.

  Find the two integers.

  (F p173, F+ p172)

12 a Write 30 as a product of prime factors.

  b Write 40 as a product of prime factors.

  c Find the Highest Common Factor (HCF) of 30 and 40.

  d Find the Least Common Multiple (LCM) of 30 and 40.

  (F p366, F+ p178)

13 a Write 36 as a product of prime factors.

  b Write 90 as a product of prime factors.

  c Find the Highest Common Factor (HCF) of 36 and 90.

  d Find the Least Common Multiple (LCM) of 36 and 90.

  (F p366, F+ p178)

14 Write each expression as a power of 3.

  a $3^4 \times 3^6$ **b** $3^5 \div 3^2$ **c** $3^4 \times \dfrac{3^2}{3^3}$

  (F+ p174)

15 Here is a list of eight numbers.

  5   6   12   20   25   26   28   33

  a From the list, write

    i a square number

    ii a number that is a multiple of 7

    iii two numbers that are factors of 40

    iv two numbers with a sum of 59.

  b Tony says that '6 is a cube number because $2^3 = 6$'.

  Tony is wrong. Explain why.

  (*Edexcel Ltd., 2004*) 5 marks

See N1 for multiples and factors.

- You can use a **ratio** to compare the size of two (or more) quantities.

  The ratio 1 : 3 means the second quantity is 3 times larger than the first.

- Some ratios can be simplified by cancelling.

$$\div 3 \left(\begin{array}{c} 6 : 15 \\ 2 : \ 5 \end{array}\right) \div 3$$

- A **scale** is a ratio expressed in the form 1 : *n*.

  A map scale could be 1 : 25 000.

- You can divide a quantity in a given ratio.

  £10 divided in the ratio 2 : 3 is £4 and £6.

- Two quantities are in **direct proportion** when the ratio between the quantities is constant.

  As one quantity increases, the other quantity increases in the same proportion.

  As one quantity decreases, the other quantity decreases in the same proportion.

  If 2 sweets cost 10p, then 4 sweets will cost 20p.

  The cost is directly proportional to the number of sweets bought.

- You can use the **unitary method** to solve direct proportion problems.

  This method first finds the value of 1 unit.

- A **rate** compares a quantity with one unit of another quantity.

  Speed can be measured in kilometres per hour.

- You can use conversion rates and exchange rates to convert between two different quantities.

  1 kilogram (kg) = 2.2 pounds (lb)

  10 kilograms (kg) = 22 pounds (lb)

Keywords

Direct proportion
Rate
Ratio
Scale
Unitary method

Real-life is 25 000 times larger than the map.

See S6 for enlargements.

Graph to show cost of sweets

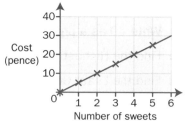

2 : 10 = 1 : 5
4 : 20 = 1 : 5

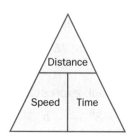

Kilogram–pound conversion graph

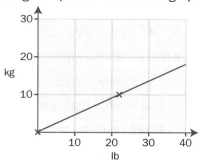

See A8 for conversions with graphs.

See S8 for conversions between metric and imperial units.

A model car is 10 cm long. The length of the actual car is 3.5 m. Calculate the scale as a ratio. Give your answer in its simplest form.

←——3.5 m——→

First change metres to centimetres.
3.5 m = 350 cm
10 : 350 = 1 : 35

This is a list of ingredients for making an apple and blackberry crumble for two people.

Work out the amount of each ingredient needed to make an apple and blackberry crumble for 5 people.

	Ingredients for 2 people
	40 g plain flour
	30 g blackberries
	50 g brown sugar
	20 g butter
	2 large cooking apples

5 people	= 2 people	+ 2 people	+ 1 person	
Plain flour	= 40 g	+ 40 g	+ 20 g	= 100 g
Blackberries	= 30 g	+ 30 g	+ 15 g	= 75 g
Brown sugar	= 50 g	+ 50 g	+ 25 g	= 125 g
Butter	= 20 g	+ 20 g	+ 10 g	= 50 g
Cooking apples	= 2	+ 2	+ 1	= 5

Marie buys 5 pens costing £6.20 altogether.

a Work out the cost of 3 pens.

b How many pens can she buy with £10?

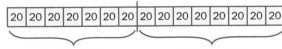

a 1 pen costs £6.20 ÷ 5 = £1.24, 3 pens cost £1.24 × 3 = £3.72

b £10 ÷ £1.24 = 8.06...

So £10 buys 8 pens with 8p left over.

8 × £1.24 = £9.92

The ratio of the heights of Mark and Adil is 7 : 8.
Adil is taller than Mark. The total of their heights is 3 metres.
Calculate Mark's height.

Total number of parts = 7 + 8 = 15
Each part = 300 cm ÷ 15 = 20 cm
Mark's height = 7 × 20 cm = 140 cm
Check: 8 × 20 cm = 160 cm
140 cm + 160 cm = 300 cm

3 m = 300 cm

20	20	20	20	20	20	20	20	20	20	20	20	20	20	20

7 × 20 = 140   8 × 20 = 160

The exchange rate for British pounds (£) and US dollars ($) is £1 = $1.95.

a Convert £40 to dollars ($).   **b** Convert $123 to pounds (£).

a £40 = 40 × 1.95 = $78   **b** $117 = $\frac{117}{1.95}$ = £60

Exercise N6

1 A digital camera costs 18 870 YEN in Japan.

In the UK, the same camera costs £90.

The exchange rate is £1 = 222 YEN.

In which country was the camera cheaper, and by how much?

(F p152, F+ p152)

2 Sarah works at a shop. She is paid £5.70 per hour.

a Calculate her pay if she works for 8 hours.

b During the 8 hours, she serves 100 customers.

On average, how many customers does she serve every hour?

c How many complete hours will she have to work to earn £200?

(F p152, F+ p154)

3 Hair shampoo is sold in two sizes.

Which size is better value for money?

You must show your working.

(F p154, F+ p146)

4 The scale on a map is 1 : 50 000.

a A road measures 4 cm on the map.

Calculate the length of the real road in kilometres.

b Two villages are 15 kilometres apart.

Calculate the distance between the villages on the map.

(F p152, 302, F+ p302, 304, 314)

5 1 mile is approximately the same as 1.6 kilometres.

a Convert 45 miles to kilometres.

b Convert 120 kilometres to miles.

The speed limit on a canal is 8 kilometres per hour.

c Calculate the speed limit in miles per hour.

(F p154, F+ p152)

6 Becca, Carly and Donna decide to go on holiday.

They rent an apartment for a week. It costs £350.

Becca stays all 7 nights, but Carly only stays 2 nights and Donna only 5 nights.

Share the cost of the rent so that each person pays according to the number of nights stayed at the apartment.

(F p370, F+ p304, 306)

7 A pizza mixture requires 150 g of wholemeal flour and 75 g of plain flour.

   a Calculate the ratio of the wholemeal flour to the plain flour.

     Give your answer as a ratio in its simplest form.

   Del wants to make 300 g of the pizza mixture.

   b Calculate the amount of wholemeal flour and plain flour that Del needs.

   (F p302, 370, F+ p302, 304)

8 Samina runs 200 metres in 25 seconds.

   Calculate her speed in metres per second.

   (F p346, F+ p154)

9 The table can be used to convert between euros (€) and pounds (£).

   a Change €3 to pounds.

   b Change €2.50 to pounds.

   c Change £1 to euros.

   (*Edexcel Ltd., 2005*) 5 marks

Euros ( )	Pounds (£)
0.10	0.08
0.20	0.16
0.50	0.40
1	0.80
2	1.60
3	2.40
4	3.20

10 The length of a coach is 15 metres.

   Jonathan makes a model of the coach.

   He uses a scale of 1 : 24.

   Work out the length, in centimetres, of the model coach.

   (*Edexcel Ltd., 2005*) 2 marks

11 Michael buys 3 files.

   The total cost of these 3 files is £5.40.

   Work out the total cost of 7 of these files.

   (*Edexcel Ltd., 2005*) 3 marks

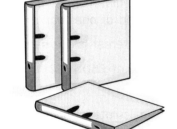

12 Here are the ingredients needed to make 500 ml of custard.

   a Work out the amount of sugar needed to make 2000 ml of custard.

   b Work out the amount of milk needed to make 750 ml of custard.

   (*Edexcel Ltd., 2005*) 4 marks

> **Custard**
> **makes 500 ml**
> 400 ml of milk
> 3 large egg yolks
> 50 g sugar
> 2 teaspoons of cornflour

- You calculate a **percentage** of an amount using
  — equivalent fractions

  $$45\% \text{ of } £30 = \frac{45}{100} \times \frac{30}{1}$$

  — equivalent decimals

  $$45\% \text{ of } £30 = 0.45 \times £30$$

  — mental arithmetic, e.g. using 10% to find other percentages.

  $$45\% = 10\% + 10\% + 10\% + 10\% + 5\%$$

See N2.
$$10\% = \frac{1}{10}$$

Keywords
Compound interest
Discount
Multiplier
Percentage
Percentage change
Simple interest

- You increase an amount by a percentage by
  — working out the increase and adding it to the original amount

  Increase 40 kg by 5%   40 kg + 2 kg = 42 kg

  5% of 40 kg = 2 kg

  — using a **multiplier**.

  Increase 40 kg by 5%   40 kg × 1.05 = 42 kg

  Increase means 100% + 5%
  5% = 0.05

- You decrease an amount by a percentage by
  — working out the decrease and subtracting it from the
     original amount

  Decrease £30 by 10%   £30 − £3 = £27

  10% of £30 = £3

  — using a multiplier.

  Decrease £30 by 10%   £30 × 0.9 = £27

  Decrease means 100% − 10%
  10% = 0.1

- VAT is a tax added to a bill or invoice.

  The rate of VAT is usually 17.5%.

- A **discount** is the amount of money taken off a price.

  A 10% discount on £30 is £3.

- To calculate **simple interest** you multiply the interest earned at
  the end of one year by the number of years.

  The interest is the same each year and remains unchanged.

  4% of £50 = £2

  Year 1 interest = £2
  Year 2 interest = £2
  and so on ...

- To calculate **compound interest** you work out the interest earned
  at the end of each year and add it on to find the new total.

  The interest is not the same each year: it increases each year.

  4% of £50 = £2   New total = £52

  4% of £52 = £2.08   New total = £54.08

  Interest after two years = £4.08

  Year 1 interest = £2
  Year 2 interest = £2.08
  and so on ...

- You can work out the **percentage change** by calculating the
  change as a percentage of the original value.

  Examples of percentage change are percentage loss,
  percentage profit and rate of inflation.

  You can also use the multiplier to find
  the change as a percentage.

Example

Calculate 35% of 50 centimetres.

10% of 50 cm $= \frac{1}{10}$ of 50 cm = 5 cm

5% = 2.5 cm

35% = 10% + 10% + 10% + 5% = 5 cm + 5 cm + 5 cm + 2.5 cm
$\qquad$ = 17.5 cm

See N2

$10\% = \frac{1}{10}$

Example

A pair of hiking boots usually costs £85.

During the sale there is a 6% discount.

Calculate the sale price of the boots.

0.06 × £85 = £5.10 $\qquad$ *or* $\quad$ 0.94 × £85 = £79.90

£85 − £5.10 = £79.90

Example

The cost of 1 cubic metre of concrete increases by 4% each year.

Today it costs £125.

Rob wants to know what the cost of a cubic metre of concrete will be in 2 years.

He calculates 8% of £125 and adds it (£10) to £125 to give £135.

This is wrong.

Explain why and work out the correct price.

8% of £125 = £10

4% for two years is NOT the same as 8% for one year.

It should be 4% of £125, then 4% of the new price.

125 × 1.04 = £130 $\qquad$ *or* $\qquad$ 0.04 × £125 = £5

130 × 1.04 = £135.20 $\qquad\qquad\qquad$ 0.04 × £130 = £5.20

$\qquad\qquad\qquad\qquad\qquad\qquad\qquad$ £130 + £5.20 = £135.20

Remember to add £5.20 to £130, NOT £125.

Example

A loaf of bread costs 84p today.

Last year the same type of loaf cost 80p.

Calculate the percentage increase.

84 ÷ 80 = 1.05 $\qquad$ *or* $\quad$ Increase = 84p − 80p = 4p

Multiplier is 1.05 $\qquad\qquad$ Increase as a fraction $= \frac{4}{80}$

Increase as a percentage = 5% $\quad$ Increase as a decimal = 0.05

$\qquad\qquad\qquad\qquad\qquad\qquad$ Increase as a percentage = 5%

Express as a fraction dividing by the original amount.

See N2 for equivalents.

Exercise N7

1 Copy and complete the table to find the VAT payable on a bill for £60.

Percentage of £60	Amount
10%	
5%	
2.5%	
17.5%	

(F p258, F+ p256)

2 Rearrange these cards to make three correct statements.

75% of	£315	= £246
60% of	£332	= £249
80% of	£410	= £252

(F p258, F+ p256)

3 A cereal packet normally contains 500 g of corn flakes.

For a special promotion, packets are made with 8% extra.

Calculate the weight of the larger packet.

(F p260, F+ p258)

4 The same book is sold in Shop A and in Shop B.

In Shop A, the book costs £8, but the price is increased by 5%.

In Shop B, the book costs £12.60, but there is a discount of $\frac{1}{3}$ off the price.

Calculate the new price of the book in

a Shop A **b** Shop B.

(F p260, F+ p258)

Shop A
5% increase on all our low prices

Shop B
$\frac{1}{3}$ off Prices slashed

5 A 3-piece suite consisting of two chairs and a settee costs £840.

One method of payment is a 5% deposit and then 24 monthly payments of £34.50.

Calculate

a 5% of £840

b the total of 24 payments of £34.50

c the extra cost of using the deposit and monthly payment method.

(F p258, F+ p256)

6 On Wednesday, the number of visitors at a museum was 672.

On the previous day, Tuesday, the number of visitors was 640.

a Find a decimal to complete this statement

$$640 \times \ldots\ldots\ldots = 672$$

b Calculate the percentage increase.

(F p260, F+ p258)

7 A typical shopping basket of food costs £26.50.

Last year the same food cost £25.

Calculate

a the price rise

b the rate of inflation as a percentage.

(F+ p260)

8 Linda puts £500 into a building society account.

Each year the building society pays a rate of interest of 4%.

Work out the amount of money in Linda's account after 2 years.

(F+ p262)

'Each year' means compound interest.

9 Martin cleaned his swimming pool.

He hired a cleaning machine to do this job.

The cost of hiring the cleaning machine was

      £35.50 for the first day

then   £18.25 for each extra day.

Martin's total cost of hiring the machine was £163.25.

a For how many days did Martin hire the machine?

Martin had to buy some cleaning materials.

The cost of the cleaning materials was £64.00 plus VAT at $17\frac{1}{2}$%.

b Work out the total cost of the cleaning materials.

Martin filled the pool with 54 000 gallons of water.

He paid £2.38 for every 1000 gallons of water.

c Work out the total amount he paid for 54 000 gallons of water.

See N6 for direct proportion.

(*Edexcel Ltd., 2004*) 7 marks

10 Ben bought a car for £12 000.

Each year the value of the car depreciated by 10%.

Work out the value of the car two years after he bought it.

(*Edexcel Ltd., 2003*) 3 marks

- You multiply decimal numbers by 10, 100 or 1000 by moving each digit 1, 2 or 3 places to the left.

$43.26 \times 10 = 432.6$

H	T	U	.	$\frac{1}{10}$	$\frac{1}{100}$	$\frac{1}{1000}$
	4	3	.	2	6	
4	3	2	.	6		

<blockquote>
Keywords

Integer
Powers of 10
Standard form

Check:
$43 \times 10 = 430$
</blockquote>

- You divide decimal numbers by 10, 100 or 1000 by moving each digit 1, 2 or 3 places to the right.

$345.8 \div 100 = 3.458$

H	T	U	.	$\frac{1}{10}$	$\frac{1}{100}$	$\frac{1}{1000}$
3	4	5	.	8		
		3	.	4	5	8

Check:
$300 \div 100 = 3$

- You can use **standard form** to represent large numbers.

  Large numbers can be rewritten using **powers of 10**.

  4.8×10^3 is written in standard form.

See N5 for powers.

$4.8 \times 10 \times 10 \times 10$

- In standard form, you write a number as $A \times 10^n$.

  A is between 1 and 10 (but not including 10).

  n is an **integer**.

$1 \leqslant A < 10$

See N1 for integers.

- You may need to enter a standard form number in your calculator.

  3.56×10^8 is entered as

  The calculator display should read

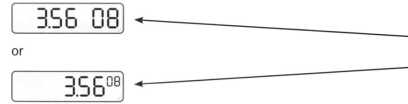

or

On some calculators EXP is written EE.

Never write this. You will lose marks.

Always write 3.56×10^8.

- You can multiply standard form numbers using the rules of powers.

  $(4 \times 10^2) \times (5 \times 10^3) = 20 \times 10^5 = 2 \times 10^6$

  Check: $400 \times 5000 = 2\,000\,000$

Multiply the numbers, but add the powers.

- You can divide standard form numbers using the rules of powers.

  $(8 \times 10^6) \div (4 \times 10^2) = 2 \times 10^4$

  Check: $8\,000\,000 \div 400 = 20\,000$

Divide the numbers, but subtract the powers.

Joshua is asked to calculate 8.67×1000.

Joshua's answer is 8.67000.

a Explain why Joshua is wrong.

b What is the correct answer?

a $8.670\,00$ is the same as 8.67.

The answer must be larger than 8.67.

Estimate, $9 \times 1000 = 9000$, which is much larger than $8.670\,00$.

b Move each digit 3 columns to give a larger number.

$8.67 \times 1000 = 8670$

Th	H	T	U .	$\frac{1}{10}$	$\frac{1}{100}$	$\frac{1}{1000}$	$\frac{1}{10000}$	$\frac{1}{100000}$
			8 . 6	7	0	0		0
			8 . 6	7				

Th	H	T	U .	$\frac{1}{10}$	$\frac{1}{100}$	$\frac{1}{1000}$	$\frac{1}{10000}$	$\frac{1}{100000}$
			8 . 6	7				
8	6	7	0					

Some dinosaurs lived 200 million years ago.

Write the number of years

a as a number

b in standard form.

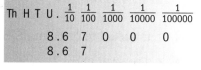

a 200 million $= 200\,000\,000$

b 2×10^8

This is the display on Edward's calculator.

Edward decided it meant $1.6 \times 1.6 \times 1.6$.

He is wrong. Explain why and work out the correct answer.

$\boxed{1.6 \quad 03}$ means $1.6 \times 10^3 = 1.6 \times 10 \times 10 \times 10$
$= 1.6 \times 1000$
$= 1600$

If $p = 1.3 \times 10^4$ and $q = 8.71 \times 10^1$

calculate **a** pq **b** $\dfrac{p}{q}$

Give your answers in standard form to 2 significant figures.

a $pq = 1.3 \times 10^4 \times 8.71 \times 10^1$
$= (1.3 \times 8.71) \times (10^4 \times 10^1)$
$= 11.323 \times 10^5$
$= 1.1323 \times 10^6$
$= 1.1 \times 10^6$ (to 2 significant figures)

b $\dfrac{p}{q} = (1.3 \times 10^4) \div (8.71 \times 10^1)$
$= (1.3 \div 8.71) \times (10^4 \div 10^1)$
$= 0.149\,253\,73 \times 10^3$
$= 149.253\,73$
$= 1.5 \times 10^2$ (to 2 significant figures)

$p = 1.3 \times 10^4 = 13\,000$
$q = 8.71 \times 10^1 = 87.1$

a $pq = 13\,000 \times 87.1$
$= 1\,132\,300$
$= 1.1323 \times 10^6$
$= 1.1 \times 10^6$ (to 2 sf)

b $\dfrac{p}{q} = 13\,000 \div 87.1$
$= 149.253\,73$
$= 1.5 \times 10^2$ (to 2 sf)

31

Exercise N8

1 Write the answers to

  a 4.5×100 **b** 0.3×1000 **c** 18.05×10

  d $0.75 \div 10$ **e** $813 \div 100$ **f** $6 \div 1000$

(F p174, F+ p174)

2 Nyah is asked to calculate $8.67 \div 10$.

Nyah's answer is 86.7.

  a Explain why Nyah is wrong.

  b What is the correct answer?

(F p174, F+ p174)

3 Copy and complete this table. The first two lines are done for you.

Power of 10	Meaning	Number
10^1	10	10
10^2	10×10	100
10^3		
10^4		
10^5		
10^6		

See N5 for powers.

(F p174, F+ p174)

4 Calculate

  a 3.9×10^3 **b** 4.85×10^1 **c** 3.2×10^5

  d $43 \div 10^1$ **e** $3.8 \div 10^2$ **f** $310 \div 10^4$

(F p174, F+ p174)

5 Give a reason why each of these expressions in NOT written in standard form.

  a 42×10^6 **b** $3.5 \times 10^{0.5}$ **c** $8.9 \div 10^4$

(F+ p176)

6 Write these numbers in standard form.

  a 4800   **b** 962 000   **c** 567

  d 32 100   **e** 7 500 000   **f** 30 million

(F+ p176)

7 The Eiffel Tower, in Paris, was completed in 1889.

Approximately 2 500 000 rivets were used to make the tower.

  a Rewrite 2 500 000 in standard form.

The number of visitors from 1889 to 2005 was approximately 2.23×10^8.

  b Rewrite 2.23×10^8 in ordinary numbers.

(F+ p176)

8 1.5×10^6 1.05×10^6 9.8×10^5 8.9×10^5

   a Rewrite these standard form numbers as ordinary numbers.

   b Put the numbers in order of size, smallest first.

   (F+ p176)

9 An internet search engine is used to find the number of entries for **Girl** and **Boy**. The results are shown.

   a Calculate the difference between the number of entries.

   b Give your answer in standard form.

   (F+ p176)

Girl
39 000 000 entries

Boy
318 000 000 entries

Difference means subtract the two numbers.

10 Calculate $254\,000 \times 452\,000$.

   Give your answer in standard form.

   (F+ p176)

11 The table shows the distance, in kilometres, from London to other European cities.

City	Distance from London (km)
Paris	3.43×10^2
Athens	2.392×10^3
Madrid	1.261×10^3
Rome	1.444×10^3
Vienna	1.237×10^3
Geneva	7.4×10^2

   a Which city is furthest from London?

   b Write the distance from London to Paris in ordinary numbers.

   c Which city is about twice as far from London as Geneva?

   d Which city is about seven times closer to London than Athens?

   e Which city is nearest to London?

   (F+ p176)

12 If $p = 6 \times 10^5$ and $q = 1.2 \times 10^3$

   calculate

   a pq **b** $\dfrac{p}{q}$ **c** $p + q$

   Give your answers in standard form.

   (F+ p176)

13 Work out $(3.2 \times 10^5) \times (4.5 \times 10^4)$.

   Give your answer in standard form correct to 2 significant figures.

   (*Edexcel Ltd., 2005*) 2 marks

Keywords
Expression
Like terms
Simplify
Substitute
Term

● In algebra, you can use a letter to represent *any* number.

On a number line, the number that is 1 more than n is $n + 1$.

On a number line, the number that is 2 more than n is $n + 2$.

See A3 for another use.

● An **expression** is a collection of letters and numbers.

$a + 2a + b - 3b + 4$ is an expression.

● A **term** is an individual part of the expression.

In the expression $a + 2a + b - 3b + 4$, $2a$ is a term.

$2a$ means $a + a$

● Terms with the same letter are called **like terms**.

You **simplify** expressions involving addition and subtraction by collecting like terms.

$4q - q - 2q = q$

q means $1q$

● You can also simplify expressions involving multiplication and division in algebra.

$3 \times d = 3d$

$8 \times a \times b = 8ab$

$c \div 4 = \dfrac{c}{4}$

$g \times g = g^2$

$6 \times b \times b = 6b^2$

$4 \times c \times 2 = 8c$

$q \times q \times q = q^3$

The multiplication sign is missed out.

See N5 for squared and cubed numbers.

● You can **substitute** numbers into an expression and work out the value of the expression.

If $b = 8$, then $6b = 6 \times 8 = 48$

Example

The lengths of an isosceles triangle are $3a + b$, $3a + b$ and $4a + 2b$.

Calculate the perimeter of the isosceles triangle.

Give your answer in its simplest form.

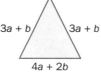

$3a + b$ $3a + b$

$4a + 2b$

See S4 for perimeter.

Perimeter $= 4a + 2b + 3a + b + 3a + b$
$= 4a + 3a + 3a + 2b + b + b$
$= 10a + 4b$

Example

a Russ has n CDs in his collection.

He buys 5 more CDs.

State the number of CDs, in terms of n, that are now in his collection.

b The length of the swimming pool is 25 metres.

Jo swims q lengths.

State the total distance she swims.

a $n + 5$ CDs

b $25 \times q = 25q$ metres

Example

Find the value of these expressions, if $p = 4$, $q = -1$, $r = \frac{1}{2}$.

a $3p + q - 2r$

b pqr

c $p^2 + q^2 + r^2$

a $3p + q - 2r = 3 \times 4 + (-1) - 2 \times \frac{1}{2}$
$= 12 - 1 - 1 = 10$

b $pqr = 4 \times -1 \times \frac{1}{2}$
$= -2$

c $p^2 + q^2 + r^2 = 4^2 + (-1)^2 + \left(\frac{1}{2}\right)^2$
$= 16 + 1 + \frac{1}{4} = 17\frac{1}{4}$

Example

Terry is asked to work out $3d^2$ when d = 5.

His calculation is $\boxed{3 \times 5^2 = 15^2 = 15 \times 15 = 225}$

This is WRONG.

Explain why Terry is wrong and calculate the correct answer.

Terry did not use **BIDMAS**.

Indices first; 5^2 means $5 \times 5 = 25$ then the Multiplication.

$3 \times 5^2 = 3 \times 25 = 75$

See N3 for BIDMAS.

Exercise A1

1 **a** There are *n* people in a room.

3 people leave the room.

In terms of *n*, how many people are still in the room?

b Ten years ago, a house was worth £*b*.

Today the house value has doubled.

In terms of *b*, write down the present value of the house.

c There are *h* balls in a bag.

A quarter of the balls are taken out.

In terms of *h*, how many balls **remain** in the bag?

(F p26, F+ p26)

2 A 10 by 10 grid is numbered from 1 to 100.

One corner of the grid is shown.

One number in the grid is given the value *n*.

In terms of *n*, write down the values of *A*, *B* and *C*.

(F p26, F+ p26)

3 Nine small equilateral triangles are fitted together as shown.

The length of each side of the small equilateral triangles is 4*a* cm.

Calculate the perimeter of the large equilateral triangle.

(F p30, F+ p26)

4 One kilogram of potatoes costs 60 pence.

Calculate the cost in pence of *y* kilograms of potatoes.

(F p26, F+ p26)

5 Nails cost 5p each.

Screws cost 10p each.

John buys *p* nails and *q* screws.

Write an expression for the total cost of the nails and the screws.

(F p26, F+ p26)

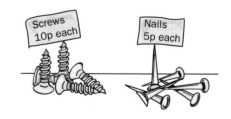

6 Work out the value of each expression, when

$x = 2$ $y = -4$ $z = \frac{1}{4}$

a $5x + y$

b $3x^2$

c $3(x + 2)^2$

See N3 for BIDMAS.

d $\frac{xy}{2}$

e xyz

(F p32, p34, F+ p182)

7 n is a positive integer.

Decide whether these expressions are odd, even or either.

a n

b $2n$

c n^2

d $n + 1$

e $2n + 1$

(F p26, F+ p26)

8 The table shows some expressions.

$2(y + y)$	$2y + y$	$2y \times 2y$	$2y + 2y$	$2 + 2y$
✓				✓

See N3 for BIDMAS.

Two of the expressions **always** have the same value as $4y$.

Copy the table and tick (✓) the boxes underneath the **two** expressions.

(*Edexcel Ltd., 2005*) 2 marks

9 **a** Simplify $3p + q - p + 2q$

b Simplify $3y^2 - y$

c Simplify $5c + 7d - 2c - 3d$

d Simplify $4p \times 2q$

(*Edexcel Ltd., 2005*) 6 marks

Keywords
Brackets
Common factor
Factorise
Index
Simplify

- You use powers or indices to write repeated multiplication.

  The small raised number is the power or **index**.

  $6^4 = 6 \times 6 \times 6 \times 6$

  $m^4 = m \times m \times m \times m$

See N5 for indices.

- When you multiply terms of the same letter, you add the indices.

  $e^2 \times e^3 = e^{2+3} = e^5$

  $e \times e \times e \times e \times e = e^5$

$x^a \times x^b = x^{a+b}$

- When you divide terms of the same letter, you subtract the indices.

  $e^5 \div e^3 = e^{5-3} = e^2$

  $\dfrac{e^5}{e^3} = \dfrac{\cancel{e} \times \cancel{e} \times \cancel{e} \times e \times e}{\cancel{e} \times \cancel{e} \times \cancel{e}} = e \times e = e^2$

$x^a \div x^b = x^{a-b}$

$\dfrac{x^a}{x^b} = x^{a-b}$

- You can use **brackets** in algebraic expressions.

  $3(f + 5)$ means $3 \times (f + 5)$

- To **simplify** expressions with brackets, you follow the same order of operations as in arithmetic.

  Brackets → Indices → **D**ivision & **M**ultiplication → **A**ddition & **S**ubtraction

See N3 for BIDMAS.

- You expand a single term over a bracket by multiplying pairs of terms.

  $4\,(x + 2) = 4 \times x + 4 \times 2$

- You expand a product of two brackets by multiplying pairs of terms.

  $\overset{\text{F} \quad \text{L}}{(p + 4)\,(p + 3)} = p \times p + p \times 3 + 4 \times p + 4 \times 3$

  O

F	Firsts
O	Outers
I	Inners
L	Lasts

- Factorising is the 'reverse' of expanding brackets.

  You **factorise** an expression by finding a **common factor**.

  $4x + 8 = 4(x + 2)$

  Check the factorisation by expanding the brackets.

4 is the common factor.

Example

Simplify

a $4x \times 3x^2$

b $(2x)^3$

c $\dfrac{x^6}{x^2}$

---

a $4x \times 3x^2 = 4 \times 3 \times x \times x^2 = 12x^3$

b $(2x)^3 = 2x \times 2x \times 2x = 8x^3$

c $\dfrac{x^6}{x^2} = \dfrac{x \times x \times x \times x \times x \times x = x^4}{x \times x}$

Example

Multiply out the brackets in each expression.

a $4(t - 5)$

b $t(t - 5)$

c $4t(t - 5)$

---

a $4(t - 5) = 4 \times t - 4 \times 5 = 4t - 20$

b $t(t - 5) = t \times t - t \times 5 = t^2 - 5t$

c $4t(t - 5) = 4t \times t - 4t \times 5 = 4t^2 - 20t$

Example

Expand the brackets and simplify, if possible.

a $(x + 5)(x + 4)$

b $(x - 1)(x + 3)$

---

a $(x + 5)(x + 4) = x^2 + 4x + 5x + 20 = x^2 + 9x + 20$

b $(x - 1)(x + 3) = x^2 + 3x - x - 3 = x^2 + 2x - 3$

F   Firsts
O   Outers
I   Inners
L   Lasts

Example

a Expand and simplify $(x + 3)^2$.

b Hence or otherwise, find the value of $17^2 + 6 \times 17 + 9$.

---

a $(x + 3)^2 = (x + 3)(x + 3) = x^2 + 3x + 3x + 9 = x^2 + 6x + 9$

b $x^2 + 6x + 9$ can be rewritten $\quad x^2 + 6 \times x + 9$

compare with $\qquad\qquad 17^2 + 6 \times 17 + 9 \qquad x = 17$

So $17^2 + 6 \times 17 + 9 = (17 + 3)^2 = 20^2 = 400$

Exercise A2

1   Write these repeated multiplications as indices.

  a $h \times h \times h \times h$

  b $\dfrac{m \times m \times m}{m}$

  c $\dfrac{p \times p \times p \times p}{p \times p \times p}$

(F p372, F+ p34)

2   A rectangle has a width of a cm and a length of $a + 5$ cm.

  a Write down an expression for the area of the rectangle.

  b Expand and simplify the expression for the area.

(F p372, F+ p30)

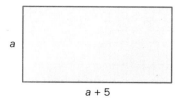

$a + 5$

3   The cards show expansions and factorisations.

  Match the cards in pairs.

$2(x - 3)$	$x(x - 3)$	$2x^2 - 3x$	$3(x - 2)$
$3x - 6$	$x(2x - 3)$	$2x - 6$	$x^2 - 3x$

(F p372, F+ p30, 34)

4   Factorise these expressions.

  a $8x - 12$

  b $x^2 + 4x$

  c $3m + 12m^2$

(F p372, F+ p34)

Find the common factor.

5   Simplify fully.

  a $s^5 \times s^4$

  b $s^8 \div s^4$

  c $\dfrac{s^3 \times s^6}{s^2}$

  d $\dfrac{4s^3 \times 5s^2}{2s}$

  e $(2s)^3$

(F+ p28)

6 Expand the brackets and simplify the expressions.

a $(x + 3)(x + 2)$

b $(x - 2)(x + 3)$

c $(x + 2)(x - 4)$

d $(x - 3)(x - 4)$

e $(x + 2)^2$

(F+ p30)

Use FOIL.

7 a Expand and simplify

$(x + y)^2$

b Hence or otherwise find the value of

$3.5^2 + 2 \times 3.5 \times 6.5 + 6.5^2$

(F+ p30)

Use FOIL.

8 a Expand the brackets and simplify the expression

$(x + 1)(x - 1)$

b Hence or otherwise, calculate the value of

$99^2 - 1$

(F+ p30)

Use FOIL.

9 Simplify fully

a $(p^3)^3$

b $\dfrac{3q^4 \times 2q^5}{q^3}$

(*Edexcel Ltd., 2003*) 3 marks

10 a Expand and simplify $(x + 7)(x - 4)$.

b Expand $y(y^3 + 2y)$.

c Factorise $p^2 + 6p$.

d Factorise completely $6x^2 - 9xy$.

(*Edexcel Ltd., 2005*) 8 marks

- An **equation** links two or more expressions using an equals (=) sign.

  $4x + 1 = 9$ is an equation.

- You can use a letter to represent particular values in an equation.

  $2b = 6$ means b has to be 3.

Keywords
Balance
Check
Equation
Inverse
Operation
Solve
Substitute

- You can **solve** equations using **inverse** function machines.

  For $3x + 5$

  $x \rightarrow \boxed{\times 3} \rightarrow 3x \rightarrow \boxed{+ 5} \rightarrow 3x + 5$

  $x \leftarrow \boxed{\div 3} \leftarrow 3x \leftarrow \boxed{- 5} \leftarrow 3x + 5$

Operation		Inverse
addition	$\rightarrow$	subtraction
subtraction	$\rightarrow$	addition
multiplication	$\rightarrow$	division
division	$\rightarrow$	multiplication

- You can solve equations using the balance method.

  An equation remains balanced if you do the same to both sides.

  You can

  — add the same number to both sides

  — subtract the same number from both sides

  — multiply both sides by the same number

  — divide both sides by the same number

  — square root both sides of the equation.

  See N5 for square root.

- Whichever method you use to solve the equation, you can **check** your answer by substitution.

  You **substitute** the value back into the equation and the equation should balance.

Solving	$2b + 4 = 9$
	$2b = 5$
	$b = 2.5$
Checking	$2 \times 2.5 + 4 = 9$ ✓

Example

Solve $5x - 6 = 9$

Balance method

	$5x - 6 = 9$
+ 6 to both sides	$5x - 6 + 6 = 9 + 6$
	$5x = 15$
÷ 5 both sides	$\dfrac{5x}{5} = \dfrac{15}{5}$
	$x = 3$

Check: $5 \times 3 - 6 = 9$ ✓

Inverse function method

$x \rightarrow \boxed{\times 5} \rightarrow 5x \rightarrow \boxed{- 6} \rightarrow 5x - 6$

$3 \leftarrow \boxed{\div 5} \leftarrow 15 \leftarrow \boxed{+ 6} \leftarrow 9$

$x = 3$

Check: $5 \times 3 - 6 = 9$ ✓

Example

The angles in an isosceles triangle are $2x°$, $2x°$ and $70°$.

Calculate   **a** the value of x

               b each angle in the triangle.

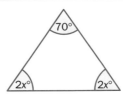

See S1 for the sum of angles in a triangle.

Balance method

a   Angles in a triangle add to $180°$.
$$2x + 2x + 70 = 180$$
$$4x + 70 = 180$$
-70 from both sides $\quad 4x + 70 - 70 = 180 - 70$
$$4x = 110$$
$\div 4$ both sides $\qquad\qquad \dfrac{4x}{4} = \dfrac{110}{4}$
$$x = 27.5°$$
b $\qquad\qquad\qquad\qquad\qquad 2x = 2 \times 27.5°$
$$2x = 55°$$
So the angles are $55°$, $55°$ and $70°$
Check: $55° + 55° + 70° = 180°$ ✓

Inverse function method

a   Angles in a triangle add to $180°$.
$$2x + 2x + 70 = 180$$
$$4x + 70 = 180$$
$$x \to \boxed{\times 4} \to 4x \to \boxed{+70} \to 4x + 70$$
$$27.5 \leftarrow \boxed{\div 4} \leftarrow 110 \leftarrow \boxed{-70} \leftarrow 180$$
$$x = 27.5°$$
b $\qquad\qquad\qquad 2x = 2 \times 27.5°$
$$2x = 55°$$
So the angles are $55°$, $55°$ and $70°$
Check: $55° + 55° + 70° = 180°$ ✓

Example

Solve $3(x - 4) = x + 2$

$$3(x - 4) = x + 2$$
$$3x - 12 = x + 2$$
$-x$ from both sides $\quad 3x - x - 12 = x - x + 2$
$$2x - 12 = 2$$
$+12$ to both sides $\quad 2x - 12 + 12 = 2 + 12$
$$2x = 14$$
$\div 2$ both sides $\qquad\qquad \dfrac{2x}{2} = \dfrac{14}{2}$
$$x = 7$$

The inverse function method cannot be used to solve this equation.

Check: $3(7 - 4) = 7 + 2$
$\qquad\qquad 3 \times 3 = 9$ ✓

Example

The inverse function method cannot be used to solve this equation.

Solve $4 = \dfrac{20}{y}$

$$4 = \dfrac{20}{y}$$
$\times y$ both sides $\quad 4 \times y = \dfrac{20 \times y}{y}$
$$4y = 20$$
$\div 4$ both sides $\quad \dfrac{4y}{4} = \dfrac{20}{4}$
$$y = 5$$

Check: $4 = 20 \div 5$ ✓

Example

Solve $5x^2 = 80$

Balance method
$$5x^2 = 80$$
$\div 5$ both sides $\qquad \dfrac{5x^2}{5} = \dfrac{80}{5}$
$$x^2 = 16$$

Square root both sides $x = 4$ or -4
Check: $5 \times 4^2 = 5 \times 16 = 80$ ✓
$\qquad\quad 5 \times (-)4^2 = 5 \times 16 = 80$ ✓

Inverse function method
$$5x^2 = 80$$
$$x \to \boxed{\text{square}} \to x^2 \to \boxed{\times 5} \to 5x^2$$
$$4 \text{ or } -4 \leftarrow \boxed{\text{square root}} \leftarrow 16 \leftarrow \boxed{\div 5} \leftarrow 80$$
$$x = 4 \text{ or } -4$$
Check: $5 \times 4^2 = 5 \times 16 = 80$ ✓
$\qquad\quad 5 \times (-)4^2 = 5 \times 16 = 80$ ✓

Exercise A3

1 Alison thinks of a number.

She multiplies the number by 5.

She then adds 13.

Her answer is 48.

a Form an equation to show this information.

b Solve the equation to find Alison's number.

(F p378, F+ p54)

2 In this mathematical wall, two bricks are added to find the number on the brick above.

Another wall is created.

The numbers on the base are $3n$, 8 and $5n$, as shown.

a Calculate, in terms of n, the values of the two bricks in the middle layer.

b Construct an equation, in terms of n, using the sum of the two middle bricks and the value of the top brick.

c Solve the equation to find the value of n.

d Find the values of the bottom layer of bricks.

(F p224, 226, F+ p54)

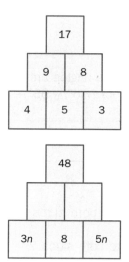

3 Heather takes her 4 children to the cinema.

It costs Heather £5 and her children £x each for the admission.

The total cost is £13.

a Write an equation to show this information.

b Solve the equation to find the cost of admission for each child.

(F p226, F+ p54)

Cost of admission
Adult   £5
Child   £x

4 Charlotte thinks of a number.

She subtracts 3 from the number, then multiplies by 5.

Copy and complete this table.

Charlotte thinks of a number	n
She subtracts 3 from the number	
She then multiplies by 5	

Her answer is 45.

a Write an equation to show this information.

b Solve the equation to find the value of n.

(F p226, F+ p54)

5 The lengths, in centimetres, of the sides of a pentagon are
$d, d, d + 1, d + 1$ and $d + 3$.

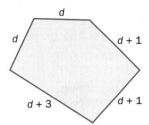

The perimeter of the pentagon is 25 cm.

a Write an equation, in terms of d, to show this information.

b Solve the equation and give the lengths of each side of the
pentagon.

(F p226, F+ p54)

6 Solve each equation.

a $4x = 24$

b $3a - 5 = 16$

c $3b - 2 = 2b + 4$

d $16 - 3x = 4$

e $4x^2 = 36$ Part **e** has two answers.

f $4(x - 1) = -2(x - 4)$

g $\dfrac{38 - x}{4} = x + 2$

(F+ p54, 220)

7 Solve $7r + 2 = 5(r - 4)$.

(Edexcel Ltd., 2003) 2 marks

8

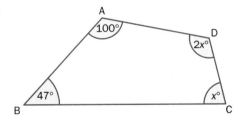

Diagram **NOT**
accurately drawn

See S1 for the sum of angles in a
quadrilateral.

ABCD is a quadrilateral.

Work out the size of the largest angle in the quadrilateral.

(Edexcel Ltd., 2004) 4 marks

- A **formula** is an equation linking two or more **variables**.

    The formula for the area of a parallelogram is

    $A = bh.$

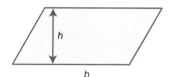

- A formula can use words or letters.

    Perimeter = 5 × length

    $P = 5a$

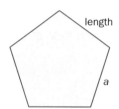

length

a

- You can **substitute** numbers into a formula.

    If $s = \frac{1}{2}(u + v) \times t$ and $u = 4$, $v = 6$, $t = 10$

    then $s = \frac{1}{2}(4 + 6) \times 10$

                $= \frac{1}{2} \times 10 \times 10$

                $= 50$

See N3 for BIDMAS.

- The **subject** of the formula is the variable on its own on one side of the equals sign.

    V is the subject of the formula $V = l \times b \times h.$

- You can change the subject of a formula using the balance method for solving equations.

    If $A = b \times h$, then making b the subject, $b = \frac{A}{h}.$

See A3 for the balance method.

Example

The cost of hiring a room is worked out using this rule.

| £20 to open the room and £8 for each hour |

The cost of hiring for h hours is £C.
Write down a formula for C in terms of h.

$C = 20 + 8 \times h$ or $C = 20 + 8h$

Example

Sami substitutes $a = 5$ into the formula $b = 3 + 4a$.

This is her working out:

$$b = 3 + 4a$$
$$= 3 + 4 \times 5$$
$$= 7 \times 5$$
$$= 35$$

a Explain why Sami's working out is WRONG.

b Calculate the correct value of b when $a = 5$.

a She did not use BIDMAS.

Multiplication is before **A**ddition.

See N3 for BIDMAS.

b $b = 3 + 4a$
$$= 3 + 4 \times 5$$
$$= 3 + 20$$
$$= 23$$

Example

$y = 4x + 2$ is the equation of a straight line.

Find the value of x when $y = 8$.

$$y = 4x + 2$$
When $y = 8$ $\quad 8 = 4x + 2$
-2 from both sides $\quad 8 - 2 = 4x + 2 - 2$
$$6 = 4x$$
$\div 4$ on both sides $\quad \dfrac{6}{4} = \dfrac{4x}{4}$
$$1.5 = x$$

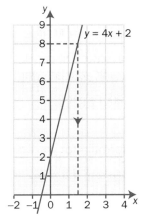

Example

The formula for the perimeter of a rectangle is

$$P = 2(a + b)$$

Rearrange the equation to make a the subject of the formula.

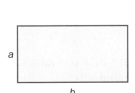

$$P = 2(a + b)$$
$$P = 2a + 2b$$
$-2b$ from both sides $\quad P - 2b = 2a + 2b - 2b$
$$P - 2b = 2a$$
$\div 2$ on both sides $\quad \dfrac{P - 2b}{2} = \dfrac{2a}{2}$
$$\dfrac{P - 2b}{2} = a$$

Exercise A4

1 A stone is dropped from the top of a well shaft.

The formula $d = 5t^2$ is used to calculate the distance, in metres, that the stone falls after t seconds.

Calculate the distance the stone falls in 10 seconds.

(F p190, F+ p186)

2 The formula for the area of a circle is Area $= \pi \times$ (radius)^2.

Mark wants to work out the area, in terms of π, for a circle of radius 6 cm.

His working out is

$$
\begin{aligned}
\text{Area} &= \pi \times \text{(radius)}^2 \\
&= \pi \times 6^2 \\
&= \pi \times 12 \\
&= 12\pi\,\text{cm}^2
\end{aligned}
$$

This is **WRONG**.

a Explain why Mark's working is wrong.

b Calculate the correct value of the area when the radius $= 6$ cm, leaving your answer in terms of π.

(F p190, F+ p186)

3 The formula for the area of a trapezium is $A = \frac{1}{2}(a + b) \times h$.

Calculate A if $a = 4.2$, $b = 5.8$ and $h = 3.6$.

(F p190, F+ p186)

4 The time taken to cook a turkey is given by the formula

$$T = 40W + 20$$

where W is the weight of the turkey in kilograms and T is the time in minutes.

a Calculate the time needed to cook a turkey weighing 2.5 kg.

b Another turkey needs to cook for 3 hours.
Calculate the weight of this turkey.

(F p190, F+ p186)

5 The time taken to iron shirts is calculated using this rule

> 5 minutes for the iron to warm then 3 minutes for each shirt

The total time taken to iron *n* shirts is *T* minutes.

Write a formula for *T* in terms of *n*.

(F p186, F+ p186)

6 The number of dots in a sequence is *d*.

The pattern number is *p*.

The rule connecting *d* and *p* is shown.

> Number of dots = add one to the pattern number, then multiply by 5

a Write a formula for *d* in terms of *p*.

b Simplify the formula.

(F p186, 372, F+ p30, 186)

7 The angles in an isosceles triangle are *a*°, *a*° and *b*°.

An equation linking *a* and *b* is $2a + b = 180$.

Make *a* the subject of the equation.

(F+ p188)

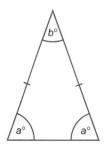

8 Make *d* the subject of the equation $C = \pi d$.

(F+ p188)

9 The cost, in pounds, of hiring a car can be worked out using this rule.

> Add 3 to the number of days' hire
> Multiply your answer by 10

The cost of hiring a car for *n* days is *C* pounds.

Write a formula for *C* in terms of *n*.

(*Edexcel Ltd., 2005*) 3 marks

10 a Solve $4(x + 3) = 6$.

b Make *t* the subject of the formula $v = u + 5t$.

(*Edexcel Ltd., 2005*) 5 marks

See A3 for solving equations.

Keywords
Counter-example
Difference
Linear
n^{th} term
Prove
Sequence
Term

- The numbers in a **sequence** follow a pattern.

  2, 4, 6, 8, 10, ... is a sequence.

  Each number in the sequence is called a **term**.

  You can see how the sequence is made by looking at the **differences** between consecutive terms.

  3,   7,   11,   15,   19, ...

  +4   +4   +4   +4

  The differences are +4.

- A term-to-term rule links one term to the next term in the sequence.

  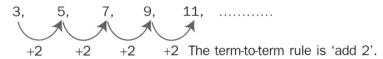

  3,   5,   7,   9,   11, ...

  +2   +2   +2   +2   The term-to-term rule is 'add 2'.

  The rule could use +, −, × and ÷.

- A position-to-term rule links a term to its position in the sequence.

position	1	2	3	4	n
term	3	5	7	9	$2n + 1$

  The position-to-term rule is often called the nth **term**.

  The nth term allows you to calculate any term of the sequence.

  The 100th term in this sequence is $2 \times 100 + 1 = 201$.

  The nth term is $2n + 1$.

- A **linear** sequence goes up (or down) in equal sized steps.

  The straight line graph of $y = 2x + 1$ represents the sequence

  3, 5, 7, 9, 11, ...

  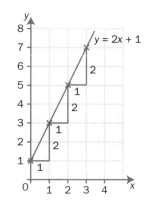

- Some sequences have special names.

  1, 4, 9, 16, 25, ... are the square numbers.

- You **prove** a statement by showing that it is true for *all* possible values of the variables.

  You cannot choose particular values to test the statement.

  You can show that a statement is false by finding one **counter-example**. This time you can choose a particular value that shows the statement is false.

  The nth term for square numbers is n^2.

Example

The *n*th term of a sequence is $4n - 1$.

Calculate the first 4 terms of the sequence.

When $n = 1$ $4n - 1 = 4 \times 1 - 1 = 3$
When $n = 2$ $4n - 1 = 4 \times 2 - 1 = 7$
When $n = 3$ $4n - 1 = 4 \times 3 - 1 = 11$
When $n = 4$ $4n - 1 = 4 \times 4 - 1 = 15$

The sequence is 3,   7,   11,   15,   ...

Example

Find the next two terms in this sequence.

2,   4,   8,   16,   32,   ...,   ...

This is not a linear sequence.

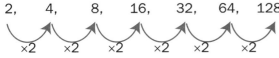

2,   4,   8,   16,   32,   64,   128

×2   ×2   ×2   ×2   ×2   ×2

Example

The number of dots in each pattern form a sequence.

Pattern 1   Pattern 2   Pattern 3   Pattern 4

a   State the number of dots in each pattern.

b   Write down an expression, in terms of *n*, for the *n*th term.

c   Use the pattern of dots to explain the *n*th term.

d   Write down a formula to link the number of dots and the pattern number.

e   Calculate the number of dots in Pattern 50.

a   Pattern 1   Pattern 2   Pattern 3   Pattern 4

3   5   7   9

+2   +2   +2

b   *n*th term is $2n + 1$ as you add 2 dots each time.

c

The 1 dot on the left is fixed and the pattern grows in steps of 2.

d $d = 2n + 1$

e   When $n = 50$ $2n + 1 = 2 \times 50 + 1 = 101$

Example

Prove the sum of two consecutive numbers is an odd number.

See A1 for consecutive numbers.

First number $= n$

Second number $= n + 1$

Sum of the numbers $= n + (n + 1) = n + n + 1 = 2n + 1$

$2n$ is an even number.

$2n + 1$ is one more than $2n$, and so must be odd.

Exercise A5

1 The first even number is 2.

  a Find the 5th even number.

  b Find the 10th even number.

  c Calculate the 50th even number.

(F p104, 106, F+ p100)

2 **a** Find the next two terms in the sequence

    2, 8, 14, 20, …, …

  b Explain why 93 is not a term in this sequence.

(F p102, F+ p100)

3 The first four patterns of dots of a sequence are shown.

Pattern 1   Pattern 2   Pattern 3   Pattern 4

  a State the number of dots in each pattern.

  b Find the number of dots in Pattern 5 and draw these dots to continue the sequence pattern.

  c Give the special name of these numbers.

(F p104, 296, F+ p98)

4 Katrina says, 'All multiples of 5 are even numbers.'

See N1 for multiples.

Find a number that can be used as a counter-example to show that this statement is false.

(F+ p190)

5 Tom says, 'All prime numbers are odd'.

See N1 for prime numbers.

Find a counter-example to show Tom is wrong.

(F+ p190)

6 Here are the first five terms of a sequence.

Position (n)	1	2	3	4	5
Term	8	15	22	29	36

Find an expression, in terms of n, for the nth term of the sequence.

(F p292, F+ p102)

7 The number of dots in each pattern form a sequence.

Pattern 1   Pattern 2   Pattern 3   Pattern 4

a State the number of dots in each pattern.

b Write an expression, in terms of n, for the nth term.

c Use the pattern of dots to explain the nth term.

d Write a formula to link the number of dots and the pattern number.

e Calculate the number of dots in Pattern 20.

(F p292, F+ p104)

8 Here are the first five terms of an arithmetic sequence.

6, 11, 16, 21, 26

Find an expression, in terms of n, for the nth term of the sequence.

(*Edexcel Ltd., 2003*) 2 marks

9 The table shows some rows of a number pattern.

Row 1	1	$= \frac{1 \times 2}{2}$
Row 2	$1 + 2$	$= \frac{2 \times 3}{2}$
Row 3	$1 + 2 + 3$	$= \frac{3 \times 4}{2}$
Row 4	$1 + 2 + 3 + 4$	$\frac{4 \times 4}{2}$
Row 5	$1 + 2 + 3 + 4 + 5$	$\frac{5 \times 4}{2}$
Row 6	$1 + 2 + 3 + 4 + 5 + 6$	$\frac{6 \times 4}{2}$
Row 7	$1 + 2 + 3 + 4 + 5 + 6 + 7$	$\frac{7 \times 4}{2}$
Row 8	$1 + 2 + 3 + 4 + 5 + 6 + 7 + 8$	$\frac{8 \times 4}{2}$

Copy the table.

a Complete row 4 of the number pattern.

b Complete row 8 of the number pattern.

c Work out the sum of the first 100 whole numbers.

d Write down an expression, in terms of n, for the sum of the first n whole numbers.

(*Edexcel Ltd., 2003*) 5 marks

- You use one of these signs to show the relationship between two sides of an inequality.

< less than
≤ less than or equal to
> greater than
≥ greater than or equal to

Keywords
Estimate
Greater than
Inequality
Less than
Systematic
Trial and improvement

5 < 7 means
5 is less than 7

- You can show inequalities on a number line.

$x < 3$	x is less than 3	
$x \leqslant 2$	x is less than or equal to 2	
$x > 1$	x is greater than 1	
$x \geqslant -1$	x is greater or equal to -1	

- You can combine two inequalities.

  $x \geqslant 1$ and $x < 4$

  can be combined to give

  $1 \leqslant x < 4$

- In an equation, the left hand side equals the right hand side.

  $2x + 7 = 9$ is an equation.

  Solving this equation gives a particular value, $x = 1$.

- In an inequality, the left hand side and the right hand side are not necessarily equal.

  $2x + 7 > 9$ is an inequality.

  Solving an inequality usually gives a range of values.

- Some equations, for example $x^3 + x = 10$, cannot be solved by inverse function machines or the balance method.

  You can find a solution using **trial and improvement**.

  In this method, you estimate a solution and substitute your **estimate** into the equation.

  If your estimate is not good enough, you improve it and try again.

  You need to be **systematic** with your estimates.

See A3 for solving equations.

Example

x is an integer and $-2 < x \leqslant 3$.

Show the inequality on a number line and write down the possible values of x.

An integer is a whole number.

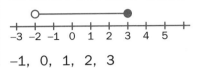

$-1, \ 0, \ 1, \ 2, \ 3$

Not -2

Example

Solve the inequality $2x + 1 > 5$.

$$2x + 1 > 5$$

Subtract 1 from both sides $2x + 1 - 1 > 5 - 1$

$$2x > 4$$

Divide both sides by 2 $\dfrac{2x}{2} > \dfrac{4}{2}$

$$x > 2$$

Example

Solve the inequality $-2 \leqslant 2y < 8$.

Separate into two inequalities $-2 \leqslant 2y$ and $2y < 8$

Divide both sides by 2 $\dfrac{-2}{2} \leqslant \dfrac{2y}{2}$ and $\dfrac{2y}{2} < \dfrac{8}{2}$

$-1 \leqslant y$ and $y < 4$

So $-1 \leqslant y < 4$

Example

The equation $x^2 + x = 4$ has a solution between 1 and 2.

$1 < x < 2$

Find this value of x giving your answer correct to 1 decimal place.

x	x^2	$x^2 + x$	Too big or too small
1	1	2	too small
2	4	6	too big
1.5	2.25	3.75	too small
1.6	2.56	4.16	too big
1.55	2.4025	3.9525	too small

This line is essential.

too small   too small   too big

1.5   1.55   1.6

$1.55 < x < 1.6$

$x = 1.6$ (to 1 decimal place)

Exercise A6

1 Match each inequality with the correct number line.

a $-2 < x \leqslant 2$

A

b $x > -2$

B

c $-2 \leqslant x \leqslant 2$

C

d $x < 2$

D

(F p374, F+ p56, 58)

2 List the integers that satisfy each of these inequalities.

a $-1 \leqslant x < 2$

b $0 < x \leqslant 3$

c $-3 < x \leqslant 0$

(F p374, F+ p58)

3 Solve each inequality.

a $3x + 5 \geqslant 17$

b $4x - 3 > 11$

c $5x + 13 \leqslant 3$

d $7y > 4y + 9$

e $5x + 3 > 3x + 7$

(F p374, F+ p56)

4 Solve the inequality $6 < 3y < 18$.

(F p374, F+ p58)

5 The equation $x^2 + 2x = 20$ has a solution between 3 and 4.

Copy and complete the table to find this solution correct to one decimal place.

x	x^2	$x^2 + 2x$	Too big or too small
3	9	15	too small
4			
3.5			

(F+ p226)

6 The area of a square is $29\,\text{cm}^2$.

By solving the equation $x^2 = 29$ by trial and improvement, find the length of the side of the square correct to 1 decimal place.

(F+ p226)

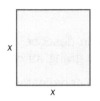

7 The equation $x^3 + x = 24$ has a solution between 2 and 3.

Copy and complete the table to find this solution correct to one decimal place.

x	x^3	$x^3 + x$	Too big or too small
2	8	10	too small
3			
2.5			

(F+ p226)

8 Blackpool Tower is 158 metres tall.

A stone is dropped from the top of the Blackpool Tower.

The formula $d = 5t^2$ is used to calculate the distance, in metres, that the stone falls after t seconds.

Use trial and improvement to solve the equation

$158 = 5t^2$

to calculate the time taken for the stone to fall to the ground.

Give your answer to 1 decimal place.

(F+ p226)

9 a Solve $5 - 3x = 2(x + 1)$.

See A3 for solving equations.

b $-3 \leq y < 3$

y is an integer

Write down all possible values of *y*.

(*Edexcel Ltd., 2005*) 5 marks

10 The equation $x^3 - 4x = 23$ has a solution between 3 and 4.

Use a trial and improvement method to find this solution.

Give your answer correct to 1 decimal place.

You must show all your working.

(*Edexcel Ltd., 2005*) 4 marks

- You can describe the position of a point on a grid by giving its **coordinates**.

  The coordinates of the point P are $(1, -2)$.

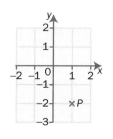

See S8 for the coordinates of the mid-point of a line.

Keywords

Coordinates
Gradient
Intercept
Parallel
Quadratic

- The equation of a vertical line is $x =$ number.

  The graph of $x = -1$ is a vertical line.

- The equation of a horizontal line is $y =$ number.

  The graph of $y = 2$ is a horizontal line.

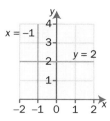

- The graph of the function $y = mx + c$ is a straight line, where m and c are numbers.

  m is the **gradient**.

  c is the **intercept** on the y-axis.

  $y = 2x + 1$ is a straight line graph with a gradient of 2 and that passes through $(0, 1)$.

  The gradient is negative when the line slopes from top left to bottom right.

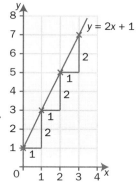

- **Parallel** lines have the same gradient.

  The straight lines $y = 4x$, $y = 4x - 1$, $y = 4x + 3$ have a gradient of 4.

- The equation of a straight line can be rearranged.

  $x + y = 3$ is the equation of a straight line.

See A4 for formulae.

- When two straight lines cross, the coordinates of the point of intersection represent the solution to both equations.

  $\left. \begin{array}{l} y = x + 1 \\ y = 2x \end{array} \right\} x = 1, y = 2$

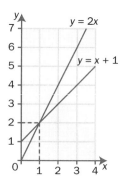

- The graph of a **quadratic** function is a parabola.

  It is a U-shaped curve.

  $y = x^2 - 2x$ is a quadratic equation.

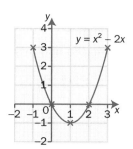

Example

The equation of a straight line is $y = 4x + 3$.

a State the gradient of the line.

b Give the coordinates of the point where the line crosses the y-axis.

A point P has coordinates $(x, 2)$ and lies on the straight line.

c Calculate the value of x.

a $\left.\begin{array}{l} y = 4x + 3 \\ y = mx + c \end{array}\right\} m = 4$ The gradient is 4.

b $\left.\begin{array}{l} y = 4x + 3 \\ y = mx + c \end{array}\right\} c = 3$ The coordinates are $(0, 3)$.

When $x = 0$,
$y = 4 \times 0 + 3 = 3$
Coordinates are $(0, 3)$.

c $y = 4x + 3$

When $y = 2$, $2 = 4x + 3$

Subtract 3 $2 - 3 = 4x + 3 - 3$

                          $-1 = 4x$

Divide by 4 $\dfrac{-1}{4} = \dfrac{4x}{4}$

                          $-\dfrac{1}{4} = x$

Example

a Copy and complete the table for $y = 3x^2$.

x	-3	-2	-1	0	1	2	3
y		12			3		

b Draw the graph of $y = 3x^2$.

c By drawing the line $y = 6$, find two values of x that satisfy the equation $3x^2 = 6$.

d Without using a calculator, solve the equation $x^2 = 2$.

a

x	-3	-2	-1	0	1	2	3
y	27	12	3	0	3	12	27

b

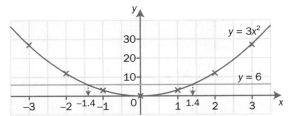

c Draw $y = 6$ on the graph.

$x = -1.4$ and $x = 1.4$

$y = 6$ is a horizontal line.

d $3x^2 = 6$

Divide by 3 $x^2 = 2$

                    $x = -1.4$ and $x = 1.4$ using the results from part **c**.

Exercise A7

1 **a** Copy and complete the table of values for $y = 2x - 1$.

x	-2	-1	0	1	2
y					3

b Draw the graph of $y = 2x - 1$.

c Use your graph to find

  i the value of y when $x = 1.5$

  ii the value of x when $y = -4$.

(F p128, F+ p124)

2 **a** Copy and complete the table of values for $x + y = 3$.

x	-1	0	1	2	3	4
y	4					

b Copy and complete the table of values for $y = 2x + 1.5$.

x	-1	0	1	2
y	-0.5			

c Draw the graphs of $x + y = 3$ and $y = 2x + 1.5$ on the same grid.

d Write down the coordinates of the point of intersection.

(F p128, 376, F+ p124, 296)

3 Match the equations with the graphs.

  a $x = 3$

  b $y = x$

  c $y = 4$

  d $y = 2x$

A 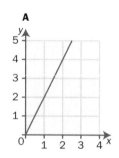 **B** 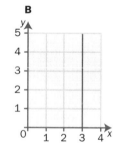 **C** 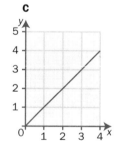 **D**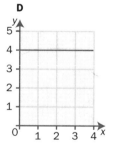

(F+ p130, 128, F+ p130, 292)

4 The equation of a straight line is $y = 4x + 3$.

Write down the equation of another straight line that will never intersect $y = 4x + 3$.

(F+ p130, 292)

5 **a** Copy and complete the table of values for $y = x^2$.

x	−3	−2	−1	0	1	2	3
y	9					4	

b Draw the graph of $y = x^2$.

c Draw the line $y = 5$ on the same grid.

d Hence or otherwise, find the **two** solutions to the equation $x^2 = 5$.

(F+ p298)

6 **a** Copy and complete the table of values for $x + y = 5$.

x	−1	0	1	2	3
y	6				2

b On the grid, draw the graph of $x + y = 5$.

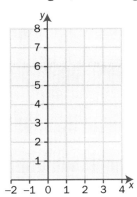

(*Edexcel Ltd., 2003*) 4 marks

7 A straight line has equation $y = \frac{1}{2}x + 1$.

The point P lies on the straight line.

P has the y-coordinate of 5.

a Find the x-coordinate of P.

See example in A4.

b Write down the equation of a different straight line that is parallel to $y = \frac{1}{2}x + 1$.

c Rearrange $y = \frac{1}{2}x + 1$ to make x the subject.

See A4 for formulae.

(*Edexcel Ltd., 2003*) 5 marks

Keywords
Conversion
Distance—time graph
Linear

- You use a **conversion** graph to convert between units of measurement.

Pound sterling–euro conversion graph

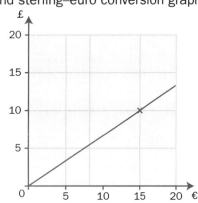

This conversion graph is constructed using an exchange rate.

You can convert from one currency to another.

See S8 for units of measurement.

- A **distance—time graph** can represent a journey.

On a distance—time graph, remaining stationary is shown as a horizontal line.

You can calculate speeds from a distance—time graph.

$$\text{Speed} = \frac{\text{distance}}{\text{time}}$$

The steeper the slope, the faster the speed.

A distance–time graph

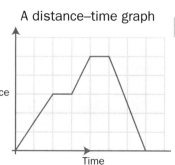

Time is always on the horizontal axis.

See N6 for speed.

- A straight line graph can be drawn to illustrate a **linear** sequence.

See A5 for sequences.

Pattern number (p)	1	2	3
Dots (d)	3	5	7

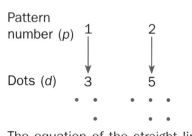

The equation of the straight line is $d = 2p + 1$.

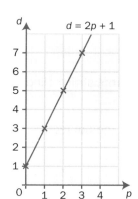

See A7 for $y = mx + c$

- You can use a graph to show how two quantities vary.

A straight line shows that a quantity is changing at a steady rate.

The steeper the slope, the faster the change.

Amount of petrol in a car during a journey

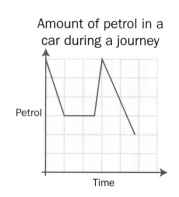

Example

These patterns are made from matchsticks.

Pattern number 1   Pattern number 2   Pattern number 3   Pattern number 4

a Draw a table to show the Pattern number (*n*) and the Number of matchsticks (*m*).

b Draw a graph to show the information.

c Write down a formula for *m* in terms of *n*.

a

Pattern number (*n*)	Number of matchsticks (*m*)
1	4
2	7
3	10
4	13

b

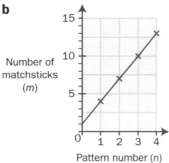

Number of matchsticks (*m*)

Pattern number (*n*)

c The differences are 3.

The gradient is 3. The y-interrept is 1

m = 3*n* + 1

Example

Two taxi firms charge fares using different rules.

Ted's Taxis

Cost (£) = 5 + number of miles

Chris's Cabs

Cost (£) = 2 × number of miles

a Draw two straight line graphs to show the charges for each firm.

b After how many miles are the charges the same for both firms?

a

Ted's Taxis

m	5	10	15	20
C	10	15	20	25

Chris's Cabs

m	5	10	15	20
C	10	20	30	40

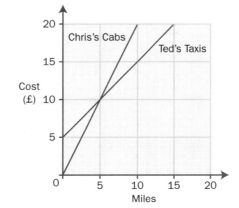

Cost (£)

Miles

b 5 miles is where the graphs intersect.

Exercise A8

1 The conversion graph shows the approximate relationship between metres and feet.

    a A tree is 9 metres tall. What is the height in feet?

    b Convert 15 feet to metres.

    c Which is shorter, 8 metres or 25 feet?

    (F p338, 340, F+ p338)

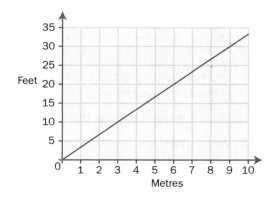

2 The graph shows the journey of a lift in a departmental store.

    a Which floor did the lift start at?

    b How long did the lift remain at Floor 3?

    c Compare the speeds when the lift is going up and down.

    (F p344, F+ p342)

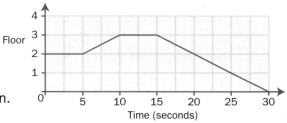

3 Sayid abseils down a rock face.

The graphs show his descent from the top to the bottom of the rock face.

Match each statement with the correct graph.

    a He descends quickly without stopping.

    b He descends slowly without stopping.

    c He descends with one rest half way down the rock face.

    d He descends in a series of small jumps and rests.

    e He starts the descent, but then refuses to move.

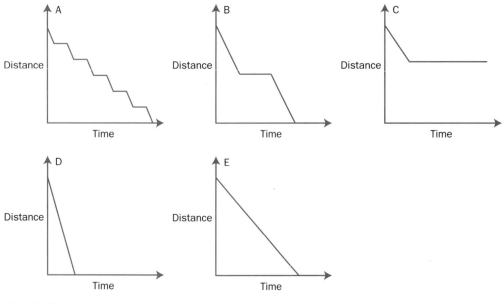

(F+ p346)

4 Sara plays in a table tennis team.

Her team wins the first 5 matches of the season.

Win	2 points
Draw	1 point
Lose	0 points

a Copy the axes and plot the <u>total</u> of points after each match. Join the points to form a straight line.

b Find the equation linking Points (*p*) with Matches (*m*).

(F p128, F+ p130, 292)

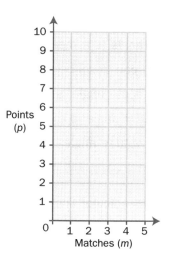

5 Here are some patterns made from pencils.

  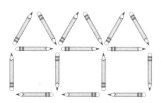

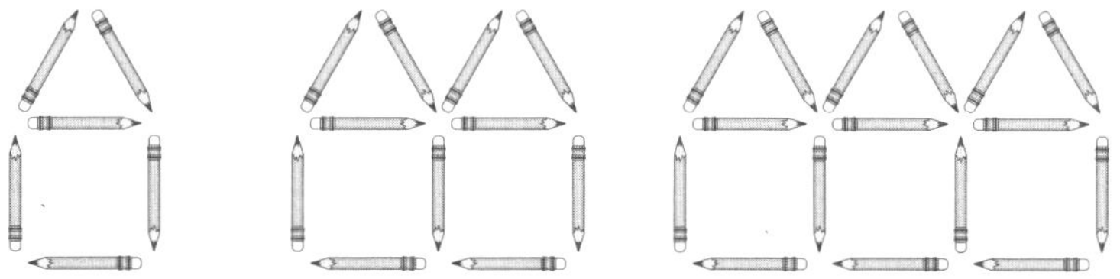

Pattern number 1   Pattern number 2   Pattern number 3

a Draw Pattern number 4.

The graph shows the number of pencils *m* in Pattern number *n*.

b Copy the graph and mark the point which shows the number of pencils used in Pattern number 4.

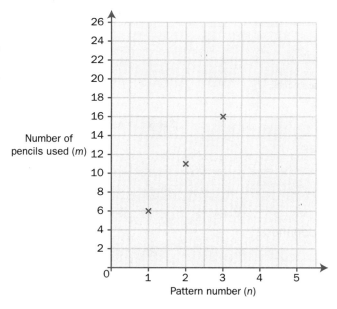

c How many pencils are used in Pattern number 10?

d Write down a formula for *m* in terms of *n*.

(*Edexcel Ltd., 2003*) 5 marks

- An **angle** is a measure of turn.

    You can describe an angle by its size.

    An acute angle is less than 90°.

    A right angle is exactly 90°.

    An obtuse angle is between 90° and 180°.

    A reflex angle is more than 180°.

Keywords
Angle
Bearing
Parallel
Perpendicular
Polygon

° means degrees.

- **Perpendicular** lines meet at right angles.

- You need to know these angle properties.

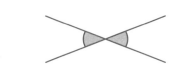

Angles at a point add to 360°.

Angles on a straight line add to 180°.

Vertically opposite angles are equal.

See S2 for types of triangles and quadrilaterals.

Angles in a triangle add to 180°.

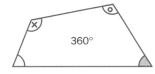

Angles in a quadrilateral add to 360°.

- **Parallel** lines are always the same distance apart.

    You show parallel lines by sets of arrows.

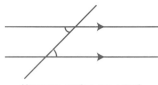

Alternate angles are equal.

Corresponding angles are equal.

- The exterior angles of any **polygon** add to 360°.

    There are 5 equal angles of 72° for a regular pentagon.

See S2 for regular polygons.

- The sum of the interior angles of any polygon depends on the number of sides.

    A hexagon has 4 triangles.

    $4 \times 180° = 720°$

    The sum of the interior angles of a hexagon is 720°.

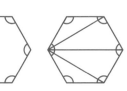

- You can give a direction using a **bearing**.

    The bearing   is measured from North

      is measured clockwise

      uses three figures.

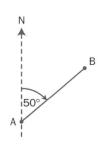

The bearing of B from A is 050°.

Example

Work out the size of the angles marked $x°$ and $y°$.

a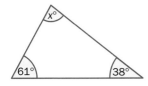

b

a Angles in a triangle add to 180°.

$61° + 38° = 99°$

$180° − 99° = 81°$

$x° = 81°$

b Angles in a quadrilateral add to 360°.

$106° + 68° + 43° = 217°$

$360° − 217° = 143°$

$y° = 143°$

Example

Calculate the value of $a°$ and $b°$.

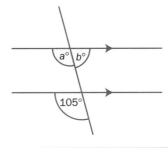

$a° = 105°$ Corresponding angles.

$b° = 75°$ Angles on a straight line add to 180°.

Example

A regular polygon is shown.

a Give the mathematical name of the polygon.

b Calculate the value of the exterior angle.

c Calculate the value of the interior angle marked $y°$.

d Explain why the polygon tessellates.

See S2 for tessellations.

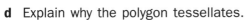

a A hexagon (it has 6 sides).

See S2 for the names of polygons.

b Sum of the 6 exterior angles is 360°.

$360° ÷ 6 = 60°$

c $180° − 60° = 120°$ Angles on a straight line.

$y° = 120°$

d $120° × 3 = 360°$

and so 3 hexagons meet at a point.

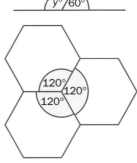

Exercise S1

1 Write down the special name for these types of angles.

a **b** **c** **d**

Right
Angle

(F p86)

2 This diagram is wrong.

Explain why.

(F p92, F+ p86)

3 Calculate the angles marked with letters.

a 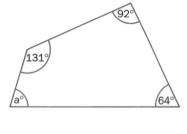 **b**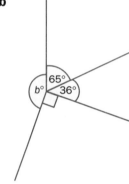

(F p350, F+ p88)   (F p90, F+ p86)

4 Choose **four** of these angles that could be the angles in the same quadrilateral.

  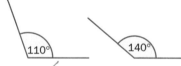

(F p350, F+ p88)

5 Calculate the size of the angles marked $a°$, $b°$ and $c°$.

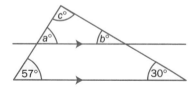

(F p384, F+ p94)

6 Measure and give the bearing of

a Doncaster from Sheffield

b Sheffield from Doncaster.

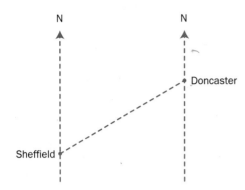

(F p248, F+ p242)

7 The diagram shows two sides of a rhombus drawn on a grid of centimetre squares.

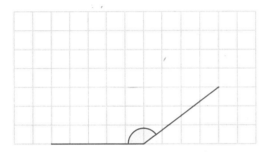

a i Measure the size of the angle between these two sides.

ii What type of angle have you measured?

b Copy and complete accurately the drawing of the rhombus.

(*Edexcel Ltd., 2005*) 3 marks

8

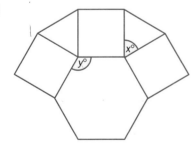

This is part of the design of a pattern found at the theatre of Diana at Alexandria.

It is made up of a regular hexagon, squares and equilateral triangles.

a Write down the size of the angle marked $x°$.

b Work out the size of the angle marked $y°$.

The area of each equilateral triangle is $2\,cm^2$.

c Work out the area of the regular hexagon.

(*Edexcel Ltd., 2003*) 5 marks

- A **polygon** is a 2-D shape with many sides and many angles.
  A triangle and a **quadrilateral** are examples of polygons.

- You need to know the properties of these triangles.

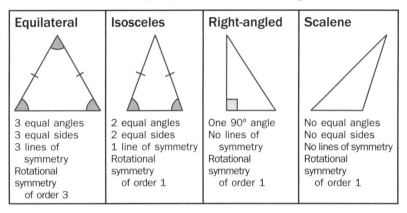

- You need to know the properties of these quadrilaterals.

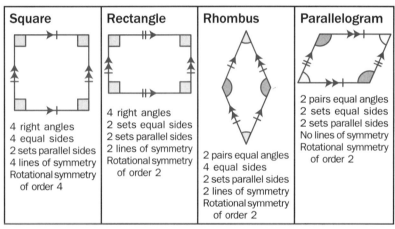

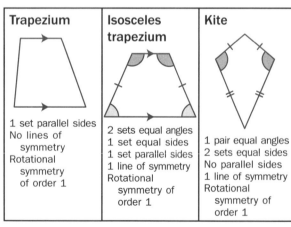

- A **regular** shape has equal sides and equal angles.
  You can construct a regular polygon by dividing a circle
  into equal parts.

- A regular polygon with *n* sides has *n* lines of **symmetry**.
  A regular polygon with *n* sides has rotational symmetry of order *n*.

- A **tessellation** is a tiling pattern with no gaps or overlaps.
  The only regular polygons that tessellate are the equilateral
  triangle, the square and the hexagon.

Keywords
Polygon
Quadrilateral
Regular
Symmetry
Tessellation

The angle sum of a triangle is 180°.

The equilateral triangle is a regular
shape as it has equal sides and equal
angles.
Each interior angle is 60°.

The angle sum of a quadrilateral is
360°.

The square is the only regular
quadrilateral, as it has 4 equal sides
and 4 equal angles.
Each interior angle is 90°.

Polygons	
Sides	Name
3	triangle
4	quadrilateral
5	pentagon
6	hexagon
7	heptagon
8	octagon
9	nonagon
10	decagon

Example

Some of the house numbers on Jack's street are shown.

a Draw any lines of symmetry on each number.

b State the order of rotational symmetry for each number.

a Line symmetry

 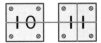

b Rotational symmetry   Order 1 Order 1 Order 2 Order 2

Give the mathematical names for the labelled parts of the circle, a to h.

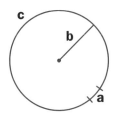 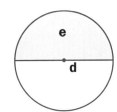 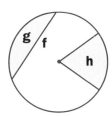

a Arc   **b** Radius   **c** Circumference

d Diameter   **e** Semicircle   **f** Chord

g Segment   **h** Sector

Two points of an isosceles right-angled triangle ABC are $A(2,2)$ and $B(-1,-1)$.

The point C is somewhere on the grid.

Give the coordinates of the two possible positions for point C.

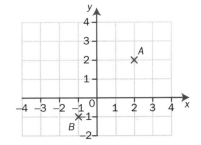

$(2,-1)$ or $(-1,2)$

(Also $(5,-1)$ and $(-1,5)$, but these points are not on the grid.)

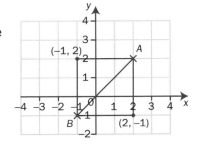

71

Exercise S2

1   The diagonals of a kite are perpendicular.

Copy and complete the table for other quadrilaterals.

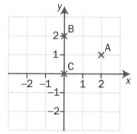

Quadrilateral	Are the diagonals perpendicular?
kite	yes
square	
rectangle	
isosceles trapezium	
parallelogram	
rhombus	

(F p196)

2   The points $A(2,1)$, $B(0,2)$ and $C(0,0)$ are marked on the grid.

Give the coordinates of a point D on the grid, so that $ABCD$ is a rhombus.

(F p196, F+ p88)

3   Calculate the missing angle in each triangle, and state the type of triangle.

a

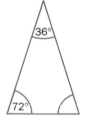

b

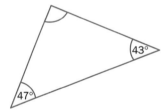

c

d

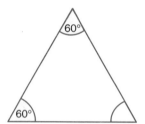

e

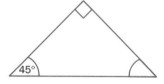

(F p194, F+ p86)

4 Draw a circle of radius 5 cm.

Divide the angle at the centre into 8 equal angles and mark the points on the circumference.

Join the points to form a polygon, as shown in the diagram.

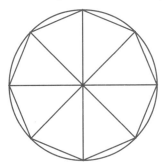

a Give the name of the regular polygon.

b Draw the lines of symmetry for the regular polygon.

c State the order of rotational symmetry.

(F p164, 166, F+ p166)

5 On a copy of the grid, show how this shape will tessellate.

You should draw at least 8 shapes.

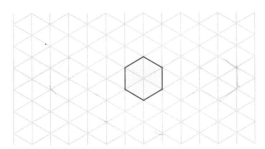

(*Edexcel Ltd., 2004*) 2 marks

6 **a** On a copy of the diagram below, shade **one** square so that the shape has exactly **one** line of symmetry.

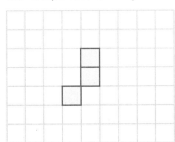

b On a copy of the diagram below, shade **one** square so that the shape has rotational symmetry of order **2**.

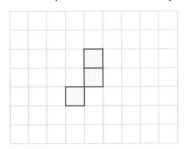

(*Edexcel Ltd., 2004*) 2 marks

- A solid is a three-dimensional (3-D) shape.

  A face is a flat surface of a solid.

  An edge is the line where two faces meet.

  A vertex is a point at which three or more edges meet.

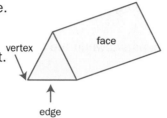

Keywords
Net
Plane of symmetry
Prism
Pyramid

The plural of vertex is vertices.

- A **prism** has a constant cross-section.

  This is a hexagonal prism.

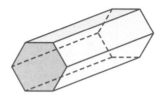

You name a prism by the shape of its cross-section.

- A **pyramid** has faces that taper to a common point.

  This is a triangular-based pyramid.

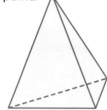

You name a pyramid by the shape of its base.

- A **net** is a 2-D shape that can be folded to form a 3-D shape.

  This is the net of a cube.

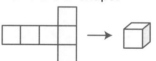

- You can draw a 3-D shape from different directions.

  The directions are plan, front elevation and side elevation.

The shape is drawn on isometric paper.

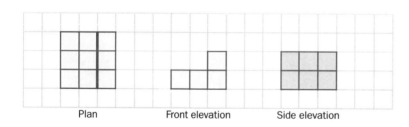

Plan   Front elevation   Side elevation

Notice the bold line in the plan, when the level of the cubes alters.

- A **plane of symmetry** divides a 3-D shape into two identical halves.

  A cuboid has 3 planes of symmetry.

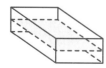 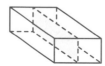 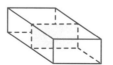

Example

This is the net of a solid.

a Draw a sketch of the solid.

b Give the mathematical name of the solid.

c State the number of faces, vertices and edges of the solid.

d When the net is folded, two other vertices meet at *P*.
Mark each of these vertices with the letter *P*.

a

b cube

c 6 faces, 8 vertices, 12 edges

d

Example

The diagram shows a 3-D shape.

a Give the mathematical name of the shape.

b Draw **one** plane of symmetry of the shape.

a Square-based pyramid.

b **One** of these diagrams.

Example

Draw the plan, front elevation and side elevation for the shape.

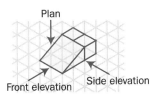

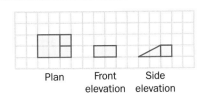

Plan   Front   Side
elevation elevation

Example

A 3 by 2 by 1 cuboid is placed on 3-D coordinate axes as shown.

Write down the coordinates, in the form (*x*,*y*,*z*), of the point *A*.

A is (2,1,3) because point *A* is 2 units along the *x*-axis

1 unit along the *y*-axis

3 units along the *z*-axis.

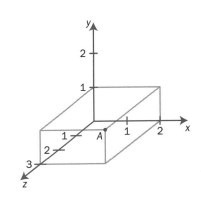

Exercise S3

1 Give the mathematical name of each of these 3-D shapes.

a 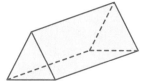   b   c   d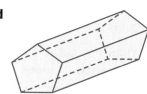

e   f   g   h

(F p202, F+ p198)

2 a A cuboid measures 2 cm by 2 cm by 3 cm.

Which of the following is a net of this cuboid?

A 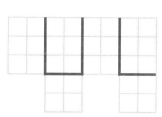   B 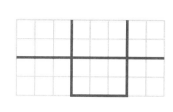   C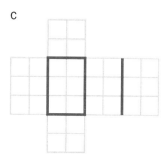

b Calculate the total surface area of the cuboid.

(F p358, F+ p198, 278)

See S4 for surface area.

3 This 3-D shape is an octahedron.

a State the number of   i faces

ii edges

iii vertices.

b Copy the diagram and draw **one** plane of symmetry of the octahedron.

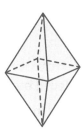

(F p202, F+ p166, 198)

4 The plan, front elevation and side elevation of a 3-D shape are shown.

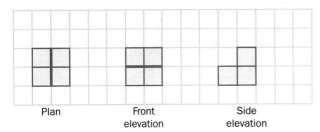

Plan   Front   Side
elevation   elevation

Draw the 3-D shape on isometric paper.

(F+ p200)

5 A 4 by 1 by 3 cuboid is placed on 3-D coordinate axes as shown.

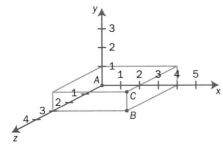

Write the coordinates, in the form (x,y,z), of the points A, B and C.

(F+ p202)

6 The diagram shows a triangular prism.

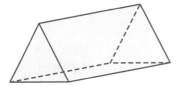

The cross-section of the prism is an equilateral triangle.

a Copy the diagram and draw in **one** plane of symmetry for the triangular prism.

b Draw a sketch of a net for the triangular prism.

c Use ruler and compasses to **construct** an equilateral triangle   See S7 for this construction.
with sides of length 6 centimetres.

You must show all construction lines.

(*Edexcel Ltd., 2005*) 6 marks

7 The diagram shows a solid object.

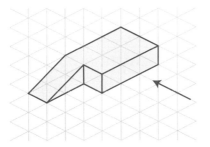

a Sketch the front elevation from the direction marked with an arrow.

b Sketch the plan of the solid object.

(*Edexcel Ltd., 2004*) 4 marks

- The **perimeter** is the distance round a 2-D shape.

  You measure perimeter in units of length, for example, centimetres.

  The perimeter of a circle is the circumference.

  $C = \pi d$ $C = 2\pi r$

$10\,mm = 1\,cm$
$100\,cm = 1\,m$

$100\,mm^2 = 1\,cm^2$
$10\,000\,cm^2 = 1\,m^2$

- The **area** is the amount of surface a 2-D shape covers.

  You measure area in squares, for example, square centimetres (cm^2).

  You calculate area using these formulae.

Rectangle	Parallelogram	Triangle

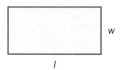 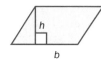 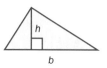

Area $= l \times w$ Area $= b \times h$ Area $= \frac{1}{2} b \times h$

Trapezium   Circle

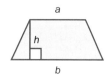

Area $= \frac{1}{2}(a + b)h$ Area $= \pi r^2$

You are given the trapezium formula in the exam.

- The **surface area** of a 3-D shape is the total area of its faces.

  The surface area is the area of the net of the shape.

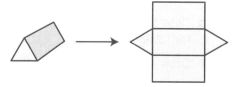

- The **volume** is the amount of space inside a 3-D shape.

  You measure volume in cubes, for example, cubic centimetres (cm^3).

  You calculate volume using these formulae.

Cuboid   Prism

See S3 for prisms.

$1000\,mm^3 = 1\,cm^3$
$1\,000\,000\,cm^3 = 1\,m^3$

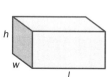 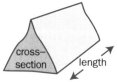

Volume $= h \times w \times l$ Volume = area of cross-section $\times$ length

You are given the prism formula in the exam.

- You can use dimensions to analyse expressions and formulae.

  πr^2 has dimensions (length)$^2 = L^2 =$ area

π is a number and has no dimensions.

Example

The area of the square is 400 cm².

Calculate the perimeter of the square.

State the units of your answer.

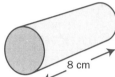

Area = 400 cm²

Area of a square = side × side = 400 cm²

Length of one side = $\sqrt{400}$ = 20 cm

Perimeter = 20 + 20 + 20 + 20 = 80 cm

Example

The cross-section of a cylinder is a circle.

The area of this circle is 10π cm².

The length of the cylinder is 8 cm.

Calculate, in terms of π, the volume of the cylinder.

8 cm

Volume of prism = area of cross-section × length

$$= 10\pi \times 8$$

$$= 80\pi \text{ cm}^3$$

Example

Change 8 cm² to mm².

1 cm

1 cm | 1 cm²

10 mm

10 mm | 100 mm²

10 mm = 1 cm

and so 100 mm² = 1 cm²

8 cm² = 8 × 100 mm² = 800 mm²

Example

l, *r* and *h* represent lengths.

π and 3 are numbers and have no dimensions.

Decide whether these expressions represent length, area or volume.

a $r + h + l$ **b** πr^2 **c** $\pi r l$

d $\frac{1}{3}\pi r^2 h$ **e** $h^2 + r^2$

a $r + h + l$ length + length + length = L + L + L = L = length

b πr^2 number × length × length = L × L = L² = area

c $\pi r l$ number × length × length = L × L = L² = area

d $\frac{1}{3}\pi r^2 h$ number × number × length × length × length =

$$L \times L \times L = L^3$$

$$= \text{volume}$$

e $h^2 + r^2$ length × length + length × length = L² + L² = L² = area

Exercise S4

1 **a** Calculate the perimeter and area of the right-angled triangle.

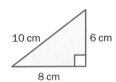

10 cm   6 cm

8 cm

Two of these triangles are placed together in different arrangements.

b Calculate the perimeter and area of each arrangement.

i

ii

iii

iv

(F p20, 280, F+ p16)

2 A circle of diameter 10 cm is drawn inside a square.

Calculate the shaded area. Use $\pi = 3.14$.

(F p278, F+ p20)

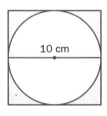

10 cm

3 A cuboid measures 3 cm by 4 cm by 6 cm.

a Calculate the total surface area of the cuboid.

b Calculate the volume of the cuboid.

(F p282, 358 F+ p278, 22)

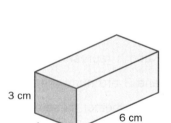

3 cm

4 cm

6 cm

4 One of these expressions gives the surface area of a sphere.

Which one?

a $4\pi r^3$ **b** $4\pi r^2$ **c** $4\pi r$

(F p286, F+ p286)

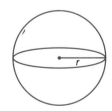

r

5 A prism has the cross-section of a trapezium.

   a Calculate the area of the trapezium.

   b Calculate the volume of the prism.

   (F p382, F+ p18, 280)

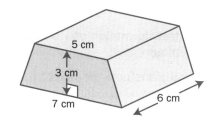

6

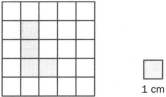

                   1 cm
        1 cm

   a i Find the area of the shaded shape.

     ii Find the perimeter of the shaded shape.

   Here is a solid prism made from centimetre cubes.

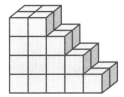

                  1 cm³

   b Find the volume of the solid prism.

   (*Edexcel Ltd., 2004*) 4 marks

7 This table shows some expressions.

   The letters x, y and z represent lengths.

   Copy the table and place a tick in the appropriate column for each
expression to show whether the expression can be used to represent
a length, an area, a volume or none of these.

Expression	Length	Area	Volume	None of these
$x + y + z$				
xyz				
$xy + yz + xz$				

(*Edexcel Ltd., 2003*) 3 marks

Keywords
Centre of rotation
Congruent
Mirror line
Reflection
Rotation
Translation

● A **transformation** can change the size and position of a shape.

You transform the object to the image.

● A **reflection** flips the shape over a **mirror line**.

Each point in the image is the same distance from the mirror line as the corresponding point in the object.

You describe a reflection by specifying the mirror line.

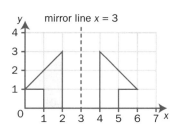

● A **rotation** turns a shape.

Each point in the object is rotated to a corresponding point in the image.

You describe a rotation by giving

— the **centre of rotation**

— the angle of rotation

— the direction of turn, either clockwise or anticlockwise.

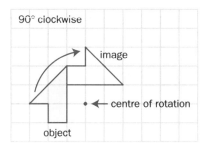

● A **translation** is a sliding movement.

Each point in the object is translated to a corresponding point in the image.

You describe a translation by giving

— the distance moved right or left

— the distance moved up or down.

You can describe a translation using a column vector $\begin{pmatrix} a \\ b \end{pmatrix}$

which means a units in the x direction

       and b units in the y direction.

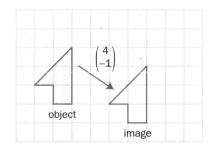

● In these transformations, the object and the image are **congruent**.

The object and the image are the same size and the same shape.

● In congruent shapes

— corresponding angles are equal

— corresponding sides are equal.

Example

Describe the transformation that maps triangle **A** onto triangle **B**.

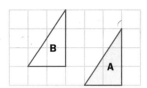

A translation of $\begin{pmatrix} -3 \\ 1 \end{pmatrix}$.

$\begin{pmatrix} -3 \\ 1 \end{pmatrix}$ means 3 to the left and 1 up.

Example

A triangle is shown on the grid.

a Give the equation of the mirror line.

b Draw the reflection of the shaded triangle in the mirror line.

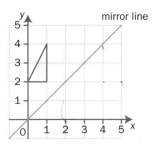

a $y = x$

b

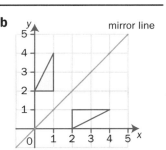

Example

Triangle **A** is rotated to triangle **B**.

a Find the coordinates of the centre of rotation.

b State the angle and direction of the rotation.

c Draw triangle **B** after a rotation of 90° about (0,1).

Label the new triangle as **C**.

d Fully describe the transformation that will map triangle **A** onto triangle **C**.

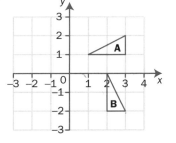

a (1,0)

c

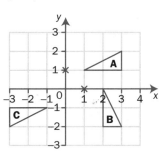

b 90° clockwise

d A rotation of 180° anticlockwise or clockwise about (0,0).

83

Exercise S5

1 a Give the equation of the mirror line for each reflection.

    i triangle **A** to triangle **B**

    ii triangle **A** to triangle **C**

    iii triangle **A** to triangle **D**

b Fully describe the transformation of triangle **D** to triangle **B** .

(F p158, 162, 314, 318, F+ p158, 162)

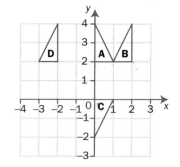

2 There are six triangles on the grid.

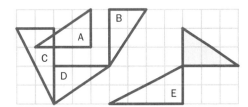

Write down the letters of the triangles that are congruent to the shaded triangle.

(F p198, F+ p164)

3 Triangle **A** is transformed to triangle **B**.

a State whether the two triangles are congruent.

b Fully describe the transformation, making sure you give the equation of the line.

(F p318, F+ p162)

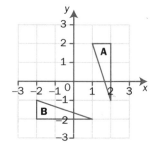

4 A shape is translated by $\begin{pmatrix} 4 \\ 2 \end{pmatrix}$.

The new shape is then translated by $\begin{pmatrix} -1 \\ 5 \end{pmatrix}$.

Give a vector that would describe both the translations as one single translation.

You can use squared paper to help you.

(F p318, F+ p162)

5 The shape **A** is shown on the grid.

a Give the mathematical name for the shape.

b Copy the diagram and draw the shape after an anticlockwise rotation of 90° about (0, 1).

    Label the shape as **B**.

c Fully describe the transformation of shape **A** to shape **C**.

(F p160, 316, F+ p160)

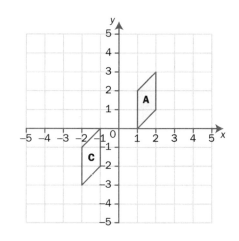

6 Triangle **A** and triangle **B** have been drawn on the grid.

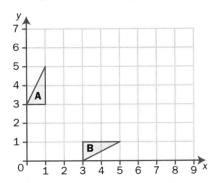

   a Copy the diagram and reflect triangle **A** in the line $x = 3$.

   Label this image **C**.

   b Describe fully the single transformation which will map triangle **A** onto triangle **B**.

   (*Edexcel Ltd., 2005*) 4 marks

7

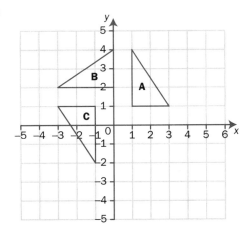

Shape **A** is rotated 90° anticlockwise, centre (0, 1), to shape **B**.

Shape **B** is rotated 90° anticlockwise, centre (0, 1), to shape **C**.

Shape **C** is rotated 90° anticlockwise, centre (0, 1), to shape **D**.

   a Copy the diagram and mark the position of shape **D**.

   b Describe the single transformation that takes shape **C** to shape **A**.

   (*Edexcel Ltd., 2003*) 2 marks

- **Similar** shapes have the same appearance but are different in size.

    One of the shapes is an enlargement of the other shape.

Any two circles are similar.
Any two squares are similar.

- In an **enlargement**, the lengths change by the same **scale factor**.

    The scale factor is the **multiplier** of the lengths.

- In an enlargement

    — corresponding angles are equal

    — corresponding lengths increase in the same proportion.

- You use corresponding lengths to calculate the scale factor.

    Scale factor $= \dfrac{\text{length of the image}}{\text{length of the object}}$

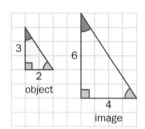

Scale factor 2

$\dfrac{4}{2} = 2$

$\dfrac{6}{3} = 2$

- An enlargement by a scale factor of less than 1 produces a smaller image.

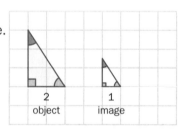

Scale factor $\dfrac{1}{2}$

$\dfrac{1}{2} = \dfrac{1}{2}$

- The position of an enlargement is fixed by the **centre of enlargement**.

- You describe an enlargement by giving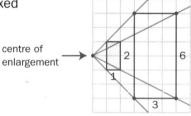

    — the scale factor

    — the centre of enlargement.

Scale factor 3

$\dfrac{6}{2} = 3$

$\dfrac{3}{1} = 3$

- In maps and scale drawings, the lengths of lines and shapes are reduced or enlarged in proportion.

    The scale factor can be written as a ratio for maps and scale drawings.

    1 : 100 is an enlargement of scale factor 100.

See N6 for map scales.

- If the scale factor for length is L, then

    — the multiplier for length is L

    — the multiplier for area is $L \times L = L^2$

    — the multiplier for volume is $L \times L \times L = L^3$.

Example

Rectangle **A** is enlarged
to give rectangle **B**.

a On the diagram, mark the centre
of enlargement.

b Calculate the scale factor.

c Calculate the ratio of the area of rectangle **A** to the area of
rectangle **B** in the form 1 : n.

a

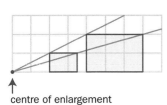

↑
centre of enlargement

b Scale factor $= \frac{2}{1} = 2$

c Ratio of the lengths is 1 : 2

Ratio of the areas is $1 : 2^2 = 1 : 4$

Check:
Area A = $1\frac{1}{2}$ Area B = 6

$1\frac{1}{2} : 6 = 1 : 4$

Example

a Enlarge the shaded triangle by scale
factor $1\frac{1}{2}$ with centre of enlargement (0,0).

b The perimeter of the shaded triangle
is 3.4 cm.

Calculate the perimeter of the enlargement.

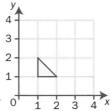

a

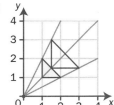

b $3.4 \times 1\frac{1}{2} = 5.1$ cm

$3.4 \times 1 = 3.4$

$3.4 \times \frac{1}{2} = 1.7$ } $3.4 + 1.7 = 5.1$

Example

Triangle **A** and triangle **B** are mathematically similar.

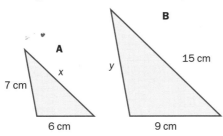

Calculate the distances x and y.

Scale factor of the enlargement of **A** to **B** $= \frac{9}{6} = 1.5$

$x = \frac{15}{1.5} = 10$ cm

$y = 7 \times 1.5 = 10.5$ cm

x is smaller than 15 cm.

y is larger than 7 cm.

Exercise S6

1 A right-angled triangle has lengths 3 cm, 4 cm and 5 cm.

    a On squared paper, draw the triangle after an enlargement with scale factor 2.

    b Calculate the perimeter and area of the enlarged shape.

    (F p322, F+ p316, 322)

2 Find the **two** triangles that are mathematically similar to this triangle.

You must show your working.

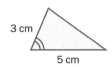

A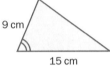

B

C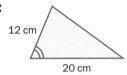

D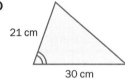

(F p386, F+ p320)

3 The diagram shows two similar triangles.

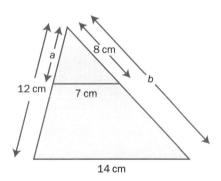

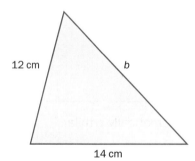

Calculate the values of *a* and *b*.

(F p386, F+ p320)

4 **a** Give the mathematical name of the shaded shape.

    b Copy the diagram and draw the enlargement of the shaded shape, scale factor $\frac{1}{2}$ and centre (0,0).

    (F+ p318)

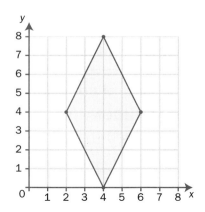

5 Cuboid **A** and cuboid **B** are mathematically similar.

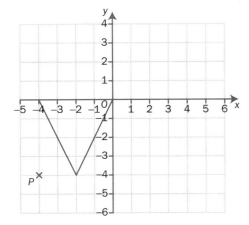

A

1 cm   3 cm
2 cm

B

The scale factor for lengths of the enlargement is 3.

a Show that the surface area of cuboid **A** is $22\,\text{cm}^2$.

b Show that the volume of cuboid **A** is $6\,\text{cm}^3$.

c Calculate the surface area of cuboid **B**.

d Calculate the volume of cuboid **B**.

See S4 for surface area and volume.

(F+ p322)

6 Copy the diagram and enlarge the shaded shape by scale factor $1\frac{1}{2}$, centre *P*.

(Edexcel Ltd., 2004) 3 marks

7

Diagram
NOT
accurately
drawn

A €20 note is a rectangle 133 mm long and 72 mm wide.

A €500 note is a rectangle 160 mm long and 82 mm wide.

Show that the two rectangles are **not** mathematically similar.

(Edexcel Ltd., 2004) 3 marks

Keywords
Bisect
Hypotenuse
Locus
Perpendicular

- You can construct triangles using a ruler, protractor and compasses.

  The information you are given decides your method of construction.

- You will always construct a unique triangle if you are given

The longest side of a right-angled triangle is called the **hypotenuse**.

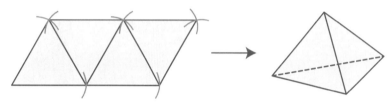

| Two sides and the angle between them (SAS) | or | Two angles and a side (ASA) | or | Right angle, the hypotenuse and a side (RHS) | or | Three sides (SSS) |

- You can construct other 2-D shapes using a ruler, protractor and compasses.

  For example, the net of a tetrahedron can be constructed using just a ruler and compasses.

See S3 for nets.

You can construct a 60° angle using this method.

- You can **bisect** angles and lines using a ruler and compasses.

Bisect means cut into two equal parts.

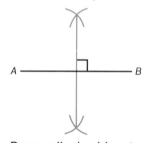

Angle bisector   Perpendicular bisector of the line segment AB

- You can construct the **perpendicular** from a point *P* on the line.

See the example.

- You can construct the perpendicular from a point *P* to the line.

See the example.

- A **locus** is the path traced out by a moving point, that moves according to a rule.

  The locus of the points that are equidistant from *A* and *B* is the perpendicular bisector of the line *AB*.

Example

This net of a 3-D shape consists of four
equilateral triangles.

a State the mathematical name of the 3-D shape.

b Use a ruler and compasses only to construct
the net.

a Tetrahedron

b

Example

Construct the perpendicular
from the point P on the line
segment *AB*.

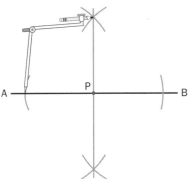

Construct the perpendicular
from the point P to the line
segment *AB*.

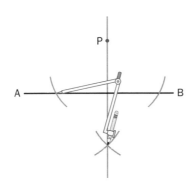

Example

Sheffield and Rotherham are 5 kilometres apart.

A shop in Sheffield delivers goods free of charge for houses within
a 2 km radius.

A shop in Rotherham delivers goods free of charge for houses
within a 4 km radius.

Using a scale of 1 cm to represent 1 km, shade the region that
shows the houses that can be delivered goods free of charge from
both shops.

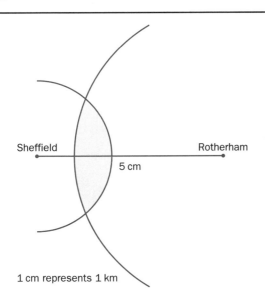

Sheffield   Rotherham

5 cm

1 cm represents 1 km

Exercise S7

1 **a** Make an accurate drawing of the triangle *ABC*.

Angle *B* = 70°

Angle *C* = 45°

BC = 6 cm

b Measure the length of *AC* on your diagram.

(F p244, F+ p244)

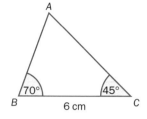

2 The net of a 3-D shape consists of four isosceles triangles and a square.

a State the mathematical name of the 3-D shape.

b Using protractor, compasses and a ruler, construct an accurate drawing of the net.

(F+ 244)

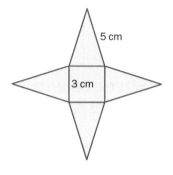

3 Copy the diagram and, using compasses and a ruler only, draw the perpendicular bisector of the line segment *AB*.

You must show your construction lines.

(F+ 246)

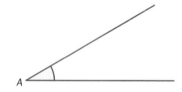

4 Copy the diagram and use compasses and a ruler only to draw the bisector of angle A.

You must show your construction lines.

(F+ p248)

5 A 5 metre length of rope is used to tether a bull in a field.

The shortest distance from a wall to the stake is 1 metre.

Use a scale of 1 cm to represent 1 metre to show the region in which the bull can move.

wall

Diagram **NOT** accurately drawn

• stake

(F+ p250)

6 This is a map of northern England.

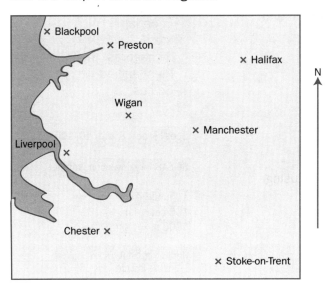

Scale: 1 cm represents 10 km

a Measure and write down the bearing of

i Halifax from Wigan

ii Preston from Manchester.

A radio station in Manchester transmits programmes.

Its programmes can be received anywhere within a distance of 30 km.

b Copy the diagram and shade the region in which the programmes can be received.

(*Edexcel Ltd., 2004*) 4 marks

7 The diagram shows a sketch of triangle *ABC*.

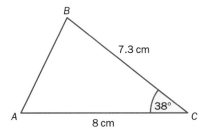

$BC = 7.3$ cm

$AC = 8$ cm

Angle $C = 38°$

a Make an accurate drawing of triangle *ABC*.

b Measure the size of angle *A* on your diagram.

(*Edexcel Ltd., 2004*) 3 marks

- You measure length, mass and capacity using **metric** and **imperial** units.

- You convert between metric units by multiplying or dividing by 10, 100, 1000, ...

- You can convert between metric and imperial units using
  — conversion graphs
  — conversion rates.

- Length is a measure of distance.

- Mass is a measure of the amount of matter in an object.
  Mass is linked to weight.

- Capacity is a measure of the volume of liquid a 3-D shape will hold.

- Measurements are only approximate.

  18 cm measured to the nearest centimetre could be between 17.5 cm and 18.5 cm.

  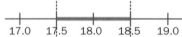

- Measuring instruments have **scales** to show measurements.
  Scales are divided into small divisions.

  2 divisions = 10°C
  1 division = 5°C

- You can use **Pythagoras' theorem** to calculate a length in a **right-angled** triangle.

  $a^2 + b^2 = c^2$

  Pythagoras' theorem enables you to calculate the distance AB between two points $A(x_1, y_1)$ and $B(x_2, y_2)$.

  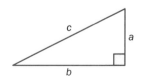

- The coordinates of the midpoint M of AB are $\dfrac{x_1 + x_2}{2}, \dfrac{y_1 + y_2}{2}$.

  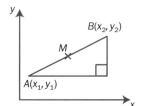

Keywords
Imperial
Metric
Pythagoras' theorem
Right-angled
Scales

See N8 for × & ÷ by 10, 100 etc.

See A8 for conversion graphs.

10 mm = 1 cm
100 cm = 1 m
1000 m = 1 km

5 miles ≈ 8 km
1 inch ≈ 2.5 cm
1 yard ≈ 1 m

1000 g = 1 kg
1000 kg = 1 tonne

1 ounce ≈ 30 g
1 kg ≈ 2.2 lb

1000 ml = 1 litre
100 cl = 1 litre

1 pint ≈ 600 ml
1.75 pints ≈ 1 litre
1 gallon ≈ 4.5 litres

The reading shows −5 °C.

Example

Alan's weight is 73 kg to the nearest kilogram.

a Write down the least possible weight.

b Write down the greatest possible weight.

a Least is 73 − 0.5 = 72.5 kg

b Greatest is 73 + 0.5 = 73.5 kg

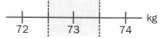

Example

A petrol gauge on a car is shown.

Write down the amount of fuel in the car.

4 divisions = 20 litres

1 division = 5 litres

The reading shows 15 litres.

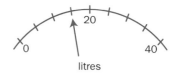

Example

An electric milk float travels at a speed of 4 metres per second.

Convert the speed to kilometres per hour.

4 metres in one second means   4 × 60 × 60 metres in one hour

$$= 14\,400 \text{ metres in one hour}$$

$$= 14.4 \text{ kilometres in one hour}$$

$$= 14.4 \text{ km per hour}$$

÷ by 1000

Example

ABC is a right-angled triangle.

$AC = 6$ cm

$CB = 8$ cm

Calculate the length AB.

Using Pythagoras' theorem,

$$AB^2 = 8^2 + 6^2$$

$$= 64 + 36 = 100$$

$$AB = \sqrt{100} = 10 \text{ cm}$$

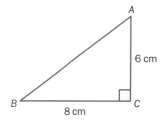

Example

The point A has coordinates $(1, 10)$.

The point B has coordinates $(9, 4)$.

Find the coordinates of the midpoint of the line segment AB.

The coordinates of M are

$$\left(\frac{1+9}{2}, \frac{10+4}{2}\right) = \left(\frac{10}{2}, \frac{14}{2}\right) = (5, 7)$$

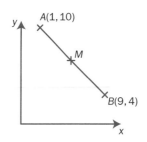

Exercise S8

1 Copy and complete the table to give a suitable unit of measurement for question.

		metric	imperial
a	The length of a path		
b	The amount of petrol in a car		
c	The weight of an apple		
d	The distance from London to Newcastle		
e	The weight of a person		

(F p14, 18, F+ p14)

2 An angle is measured with a protractor.

The angle is 132° to the nearest degree.

a Write down the least possible value for the angle.

b Write down the greatest possible value for the angle.

(F p250)

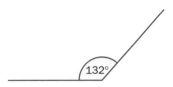

3 Sue is standing next to a tree.

a Estimate Sue's height in centimetres.

b Convert your estimate of Sue's height to metres.

c Estimate the height of the tree in metres.

(F p14, 16, F+ p14)

4 Give the reading on each scale.

a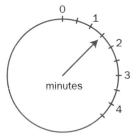

b

c

(F p250, F+ p4)

5 Estimate the reading on each scale.

a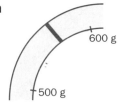

b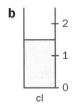

c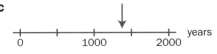

(F p250, F+ p4)

6 Angela's weight is 64 kg.

Calculate her approximate weight in pounds (lb).

(F p18, F+ p14)

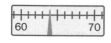

7 A right-angled triangle has lengths 5 metres, x metres and 13 metres, as shown.

Calculate the distance marked x.

(F p390, F+ p354)

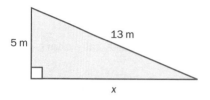

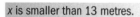

x is smaller than 13 metres.

8 The point A has coordinates $(-2, 6)$.

The point B has coordinates $(4, 0)$.

Calculate the coordinates of the midpoint of the line AB.

(F+ p358)

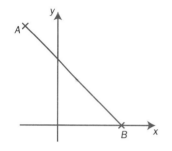

9 a Copy and complete the table by writing a sensible metric unit on each dotted line.

The first one has been done for you.

The distance from London to Birmingham	179 kilometres
The weight of a twenty pence coin	5 ------------------
The height of the tallest living man	232 ------------------
The volume of lemonade in a glass	250 --------------------

b Change 5000 metres to kilometres.

(*Edexcel Ltd., 2005*) 4 marks

10 James and Sam went on holiday by plane.

The pilot said the speed of the plane was 285 kilometres per hour.

James told Sam that 285 kilometres per hour was about the same as 80 metres per second.

Was James correct?

Show working to justify your answer.

(*Edexcel Ltd., 2005*) 3 marks

This is a conversion of units question, not a question about speed.

● You can collect information or data using a **data-collection sheet**.

A data-collection sheet allows you to ask one question and to collect all the data on one sheet.

This one is a **tally chart**.

'Do you prefer a take-away, restaurant meal or neither?'

Meal	Tally	Frequency
Take-away	𝍏	6
Restaurant	|||	4
Neither			1

$\text{𝍏} = 5$

● The **frequency table** shows the same information as the tally chart.

Meal	Frequency
Take-away	6
Restaurant	4
Neither	1

● You can collect data using a **questionnaire**.

A questionnaire gives more information, but you need one questionnaire for each person in your **survey**.

You must be careful how you word your question and response section.

Questions or response sections that are confusing will not give reliable data.

Male ☐	Female ☐
Which do you prefer?	
Take-away meal	☐
Restaurant meal	☐
Neither	☐

● A **two-way table** shows the results in more detail and links two types of data.

This one shows gender and preferred meal.

	Male	Female
Take-away	2	4
Restaurant	1	3
Neither	0	1

4 females prefer a take-away meal.

● A sample is used when you cannot collect data from all the population.

A sample of 50 students might represent a school of 1200 students.

You need to be careful how you choose the 50 students for your sample.

● In a **random sample**, each person must be equally likely to be chosen.

Picking names out of a hat is a simple way to obtain a random sample.

● The sample is **biased** if each person is not equally likely to be chosen.

Choosing the first 50 students in a register is biased, as 1150 students would not have the opportunity to take part in the survey.

● The larger the size of the sample, the more accurate the data will be.

A sample of 100 students will give more reliable data than a sample of 50 students.

'How many CDs do you own?'

CDs	Tally	Frequency
None		
1 to 20		
21 to 40		
over 40		

● You can group numerical data into class intervals to reduce the size of the data-collection sheet.

Rhiannon's questionnaire includes this question and response section.

a Make two criticisms of this part of her questionnaire.

b Rewrite the question and the response section.

How often do you have a take-away meal?
Sometimes ☐
Occasionally ☐
Seldom ☐

a The question is too vague.

The response section uses words that mean different things to different people.

b The question is factually based, over a past time period.

The response section covers all possibilities with no overlaps.

How many take-away meals did you have in the last 5 days?
None ☐
1 or 2 ☐
3 or 4 ☐
5 or more ☐

The heights of 20 plants, to the nearest centimetre, are shown.

14	45	56	31	12
67	80	45	26	7
75	34	79	20	24
59	63	66	45	34

Height (cm)	Tally	Frequency
$0 < h \leqslant 20$		
$20 < h \leqslant 40$		
$40 < h \leqslant 60$		
$60 < h \leqslant 80$		

Complete the frequency table.

Height (cm)	Tally	Frequency
$0 < h \leqslant 20$	||||	4
$20 < h \leqslant 40$	卌	5
$40 < h \leqslant 60$	卌	5
$60 < h \leqslant 80$	卌 |	6

20 is in the class interval $0 < h \leqslant 20$.

Steve is a Year 11 student. He needs to find out whether the 200 students in Year 11 at his school would like a leaving do.

He asks five of his friends. Four say 'Yes' and one says 'No'.

Steve claims 80% of the school want a leaving do.

Make two criticisms of his sampling method and suggest a better method.

Steve's method is biased, as each student of the school is not equally likely to be chosen.

The sample is too small.

He should put the name of each Year 11 student in a hat, and select about 25 names.

Exercise D1

1 Tickets to watch an Irish band called Spool are priced at £2, £5 and £10.

In one hour, tickets were sold at the following prices.

£10	£5	£10	£5	£5	£2	£10	£10
£2	£5	£5	£10	£10	£5	£2	£2
£2	£10	£2	£5	£10	£10	£5	£5

a Construct and complete a tally chart to show this information.

b How many tickets were sold in the hour?   *23*

c Calculate the total amount of money taken during the hour.

(F p62, F+ p62)

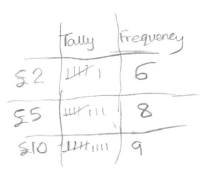

	Tally	Frequency
£2	LHT I	6
£5	LHT III	8
£10	LHT IIII	9

For part **c**, see D4.

2 Graham records the daily mileage of his car during one month.

45	9	32	(10)	24	5	(15)
37	29	0	28	30	0	35
(18)	25	(16)	43	2	31	44
(17)	8	40	23	29	(11)	(10)

a In which month did Graham carry out the survey?

b Copy and complete the frequency table.

Car mileage	Tally	Frequency
0 to 9	LHT I	6
10 to 19	LHT II	7
20 to 29	LHT I	6
30 to 39	LHT	5
40 to 49	IIII	4

c How many days did Graham use his car for less than 10 miles?

(F p68, F+ p68)

3 Linford School decide to select a Class Representative from each class to form a School Council.

Explain a method to randomly select one Class Representative from each class.

(F p401, F+ p64)

4 Nadia designs a questionnaire.

overlap and doesn't say 60 or over

Part of the questionnaire is shown.

Give two criticisms of the response section.

(F p66, F+ p66)

Which age group are you in?

0 to 20 ☐
20 to 40 ☐
40 to 60 ☐

5 The results of a survey are shown in the bar chart.

'*Do you leave your TV on standby?*'

Make a criticism of the available categories on the horizontal axis.

(F p66, F+ p66)

People might not do this

It doesn't give a specific time
scale.

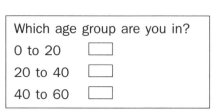

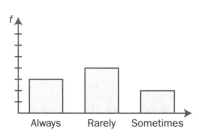

Always   Rarely   Sometimes

6 A sports club has only two sections, Tennis and Squash.

Members of the club either play tennis or squash, but not both.

The two-way table shows the membership details.

	Tennis	Squash
Children	9	3
Adults	31	7

Calculate

a the number of children in the sports club 12

b the number of members who play tennis 40

c the percentage of the club who play squash. $\dfrac{10}{50}$

(F p70, F+ p70)

7 Mr Beeton is going to open a restaurant.

He wants to know what type of restaurant people like.

He designs a questionnaire.

a Design a suitable question he could use to find out what type of restaurant people like.

He asks his family, 'Do you agree that pizza is better than pasta?'

This is **not** a good way to find out what people who might use his restaurant like to eat.

b Write down **two** reasons why this is **not** a good way to find out what people who might use his restaurant would like to eat.

(*Edexcel Ltd., 2003*) 4 marks

8 Daniel carried out a survey of his friends' favourite flavour of crisps.

Here are his results.

Plain	Chicken	Bovril	Salt & Vinegar	Plain
Salt & Vinegar	Plain	Chicken	Plain	Bovril
Plain	Chicken	Bovril	Salt & Vinegar	Bovril
Bovril	Plain	Plain	Salt & Vinegar	Plain

a Copy and complete the table to show Daniel's results.

Flavour of crisps	Tally	Frequency
Plain	⊥⊥⊥ |||	8
Chicken	|||	3
Bovril	⊥⊥⊥	5
Salt & Vinegar	||||	4

b Write down the number of Daniel's friends whose favourite flavour was Salt & Vinegar. 4

c Which was the favourite flavour of most of Daniel's friends? Plain

(*Edexcel Ltd., 2005*) 7 marks

Keywords
Bar chart
Bar-line chart
Ordered
Pictogram
Pie chart
Stem-and-leaf diagram

● You can use a **pictogram** to display data.

Symbols and fractions of symbols are used to represent the data.

Hours of sun at the weekend

Key: ☺ = 2 hours

Sat 9 hours
Sun 5 hours

● **Bar charts** can be either horizontal or vertical.

The bars have equal thickness and are separated by gaps.

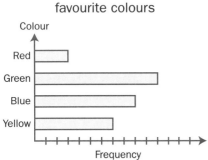

Bar chart to show Class 11P's favourite colours

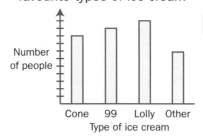

Bar chart to show the theatre group's favourite types of ice cream

The mode is Lolly — see D4.

● A **bar-line chart** uses lines instead of bars.

You can best display numerical data using a bar-line chart.

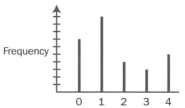

Bar-line chart to show the number of siblings of students in class 10Q

The mode is 1 — see D4.

● A **pie chart** gives a visual display of all the data.

The size of the sector angle is proportional to the frequency.

Pie chart to show the types of television providers to houses in Clarendon Road

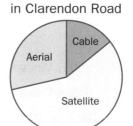

The mode is Satellite — see D4.

● You can use a **stem-and-leaf diagram** to display numerical data.

A stem-and-leaf diagram is similar to a horizontal bar chart, but with more detail.

The data is in numerical order for an **ordered** stem-and-leaf diagram.

1	3 2 4 3
2	6 3
3	8 7
4	0 3 2 0

➡

1	2 3 3 4
2	3 6
3	7 8
4	0 0 2 3

Key: | 1 | 3 | means 13

A key is essential.

Example

The numbers of houses in four streets are shown.

Street	Number of houses
Albert Street	18
Bath Road	30
Cold Way	26
Don Drive	16

a Draw a pie chart to illustrate the data.

b Calculate the percentage of houses on Albert Street.

a 18 + 30 + 26 + 16 = 90 houses

90 houses = 360°

1 house = 4°

Albert Street = 18 × 4° = 72°

Bath Road = 30 × 4° = 120°

Cold Way = 26 × 4° = 104°

Don Drive = 16 × 4° = 64°

Pie chart to show the number of houses on four streets

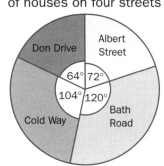

b $\frac{18}{90} = \frac{1}{5}$ = 20%

Example

The amount of rain, in centimetres, during the month of November for the last 24 years is shown.

51.3   50.6   54.8   54.0   53.1   51.3

52.1   53.8   50.1   51.6   54.2   52.4

53.6   52.8   51.2   50.2   51.9   53.0

53.1   54.9   50.3   51.0   54.6   52.8

Draw an ordered stem-and-leaf diagram from the data.

50	6 1 3 2
51	3 2 6 0 9 3
52	1 8 4 8
53	6 1 8 1 0
54	9 8 0 2 6

50	1 2 3 6
51	0 2 3 3 6 9
52	1 4 8 8
53	0 1 1 6 8
54	0 2 6 8 9

Key: 51 | 3 means 51.3

Exercise D2

1 The pictogram shows the type of fish caught in a fishing match.

Copy and complete the pictogram for this information.

Trout 9
Tench 6
Carp 7
Bream 8
Barbel 5

(F p110, F+ p110)

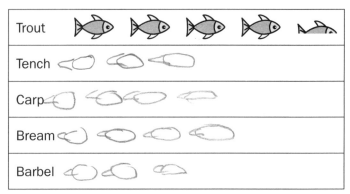

Key: = 2 fish

2 A spinner is spun 30 times and the scores are recorded.

Score	Frequency
1	11
2	0
3	9
4	7
5	3

a Show the results in a bar-line chart.

b Do you think the spinner is biased?

See D6 for biased.

(F p112, F+ p110)

3 Three salesmen at Cheap Car Garage sell 120 cars between them.

a Calculate the angle one car would represent in a pie chart.

b Calculate the angle of each category in the pie chart.

c Draw a pie chart to show the data.

(F p114, F+ p110)

Salesman	Number of cars
Steve	70
Charlie	20
Jason	30

4 Mark travels to work by train.

He counts the number of passengers for 20 journeys.

34   8   11   32   20   25   18   14   21   29

41   30   40   10   15   7   23   9   39   16

Draw an ordered stem-and-leaf diagram, using stems 0, 10, 20, 30 and 40.

Remember to show the key.

(F p116, F+ p114)

5 Mary spent £8 to buy these items at a shop.

Draw a pie chart to illustrate this information.

(F p114, F+ p110)

Notebook	£1
Pens	£3
Magazines	£4

6 The temperature in °C in a room is taken every 10 minutes for 4 hours.

21.2   20.4   22.6   20.8   23.8   20.9

21.7   24.6   24.1   23.8   24.8   24.5

21.5   23.7   21.7   22.8   20.3   22.0

24.2   22.9   24.1   23.0   23.3   24.0

Copy and complete an ordered stem-and-leaf diagram to show the data.

20	
21	
22	
23	
24	

Key: 21 | 2 | means 21.2 °C

(F p116, F+ p114)

7 The pictogram shows the number of boxes of chocolates sold last week from Monday to Friday.

Represents 20 boxes of chocolates sold

a Write down the number of boxes of chocolates sold on

i Monday 40

ii Wednesday. 42

On Saturday, 100 boxes of chocolates were sold.

b Show this on a copy of the pictogram.

On Sunday, 55 boxes of chocolates were sold.

c Show this on your copy of the pictogram.

(*Edexcel Ltd., 2003*) 4 marks

- **Discrete data** can take only exact values.

  The number of people in a car is an example of discrete data.

- **Continuous data** can take any value and cannot be measured exactly.

  The height of a person is an example of continuous data.

Keywords
Continuous data
Discrete data
Frequency polygon
Histogram
Line of best fit
Scatter graph

- You can use a bar chart to display grouped discrete data.

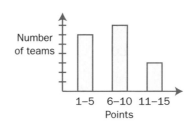

Gaps between the bars.

- You can use a **histogram** to display grouped continuous data.

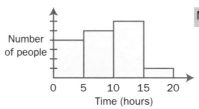

No gaps between the bars.

- You can also use a **frequency polygon** to display grouped continuous data.

  The points are plotted at the midpoints of the class intervals.

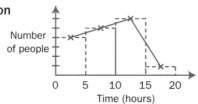

Just draw the polygon, not the dotted lines.

- A **scatter graph** is used to test if there is a linear relationship between two sets of data.

  The data is collected in pairs and plotted as coordinates.

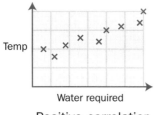

Positive correlation

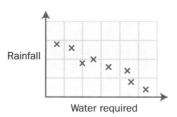

Negative correlation

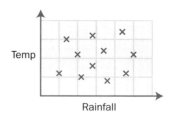

No correlation

There is a linear relationship between Temperature and Water required.

There is a linear relationship between Rainfall and Water required.

There is no linear relationship between Temperature and Rainfall.

You can draw a **line of best fit** if there is a strong linear relationship.

The line of best fit does not have to pass through (0,0).

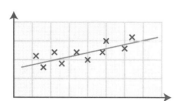

The heights of 50 sunflowers, in metres, are shown in the frequency table.

Height	Number of plants
$0 < h \leqslant 0.5$	8
$0.5 < h \leqslant 1.0$	18
$1.0 < h \leqslant 1.5$	15
$1.5 < h \leqslant 2.0$	9

Draw a **frequency diagram** to illustrate the data.

A **frequency diagram** for continuous data means either a histogram or a frequency polygon.

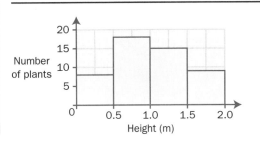

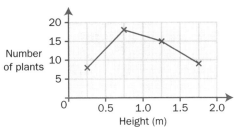

Ten students decided to record the hours they spent on revision and their maths exam mark. The results are shown.

Exam mark (%)	55	65	35	48	50	60	45	40	35	30
Hours of revision	5	6	1	3	4	6	4	2	2	0

a Draw a scatter diagram to show the results.

b Draw a line of best fit.

c Describe the relationship between the exam mark and the hours of revision.

Gareth did $5\frac{1}{2}$ hours of revision.

d Use your line of best fit to estimate Gareth's exam mark.

a, b

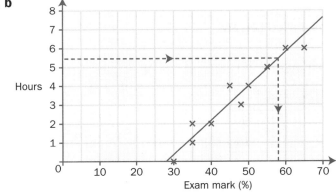

c Positive correlation. The more the students revise, the better their exam marks are. The less they revise, the worse their exam marks are.

d 58% (using the line of best fit)

Exercise D3

1 Ayesha counts the number of items in each basket at a supermarket.

The results are shown in the frequency table.

Draw a bar chart to show this information.

(F+ p112)

Number of items	Number of baskets
1–10	3
11–20	12
21–30	10
31–40	17
41–50	8

Grouped discrete data

2 The weights of 25 bags are shown in the frequency table.

Draw a frequency polygon to show this data.

(F+ p112)

Weight (kg)	Number of bags
$0 < w \leqslant 5$	0
$5 < w \leqslant 10$	2
$10 < w \leqslant 15$	5
$15 < w \leqslant 20$	3
$20 < w \leqslant 25$	6
$25 < w \leqslant 30$	9

Grouped continuous data

3

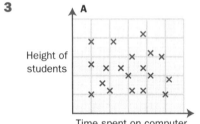
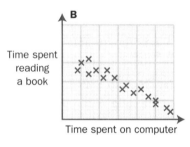
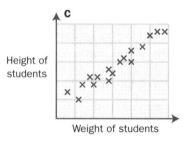

For each scatter graph,

a State the type of correlation, if any.

b State if there is a linear relationship between the two variables.

c Describe the relationship in words.

(F p394, F+ p118)

4 Ten people take part in a dancing competition.

Each contestant is awarded marks by two judges, called Len and Craig.

The table shows the marks given to each contestant.

Contestant	A	B	C	D	E	F	G	H	I	J
Len	6	10	3	8	4	2	5	9	1	7
Craig	3	4	5	7	1	8	6	2	9	10

a Draw a scatter diagram to show the results.

b State the type of correlation, if any.

c Is there a linear relationship between Len's marks and Craig's marks?

d Describe in words the relationship between Len's marks and Craig's marks.

(F p394, F+ p118)

5 All the students in Jamal's class take part in a sponsored walk.

The distance each student walks is recorded.

a Draw a histogram to show this data.

b How many students walked 5 miles or less?

c How many students walked over 6 miles?

d Calculate the number of students in Jamal's class.

e Calculate, as a percentage, the number of students who walked over 7 miles, but at most 8 miles.

(F+ p112)

Miles	Number of students
$0 < w \leq 1$	2
$1 < w \leq 2$	0
$2 < w \leq 3$	1
$3 < w \leq 4$	3
$4 < w \leq 5$	4
$5 < w \leq 6$	2
$6 < w \leq 7$	0
$7 < w \leq 8$	5
$8 < w \leq 9$	2
$9 < w \leq 10$	6

6 The scatter graph shows the mother ape's leg length and the baby ape's birth weight, for each baby ape.

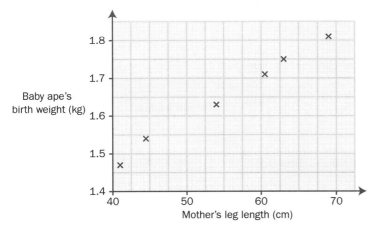

Mother's leg length (cm)

The table shows the mother's leg length and the birth weight of two more baby apes.

Mother's leg length (cm)	50	65
Baby ape's birth weight (kg)	1.6	1.75

a Copy the scatter graph and plot the information from the table.

b Describe the correlation between a mother's leg length and her baby ape's birth weight.

c Draw a line of best fit on your diagram.

A mother's leg length is 55 cm.

d Use your line of best fit to estimate the birth weight of her baby ape.

(*Edexcel Ltd., 2005*) 4 marks

Keywords
Frequency table
Mean
Median
Mode
Modal class
Range
Spread

● You can measure the **spread** of a set of numbers by calculating the **range**.

The range is the highest value minus the lowest value.

● There are three different ways to find one value to represent a set of data.

— The **mean** is the total of all the values divided by the number of values.

1.8 children is the mean number of children per family in the UK.

— The **mode** is the value that occurs the most often.

'The most frequent colour for a car is silver' would suggest the mode is silver.

— The **median** is the middle value when the data is arranged in numerical order.

The median of 0, 1, 3, 4, 5, 5, 5 is 4.

Don't forget to order the data.

● You can calculate the mean, mode and median for a **frequency table**.

Number	Frequency
1	10
2	20
3	36
4	34

See the example.

● You cannot calculate the exact mean for grouped data.

You can calculate an estimate of the mean.

Height	Frequency
$0 < h \leqslant 10$	3
$10 < h \leqslant 20$	14
$20 < h \leqslant 30$	5

Use the mid-values of each class interval.

● You cannot calculate the mode for grouped data.

You can state the **modal class**.

Number	Frequency
1–10	3
11–20	14
21–30	5
31–40	8
41–50	3

The modal class is 11–20 as this class has the highest frequency.

● You cannot calculate the median for grouped data.

You can find the class in which the median lies.

Number	Frequency
101–110	3
111–120	4
121–130	12

The median is the 10th number out of 19.

This number is in the 121–130 class interval.

Boxes of drawing pins should contain approximately 40 pins.

The contents of 20 boxes are counted.

The results are shown in the frequency table.

a Calculate the total number of drawing pins in all 20 boxes.

b Calculate the mean number of drawing pins per box.

c Calculate the median.

d State the mode.

Number of pins	Number of boxes
39	3
40	5
41	4
42	6
43	2

a $117 + 200 + 164 + 252 + 86 = 819$ pins

b $819 \div 20 = 40.95$ pins

c 41 pins (using the 10th and 11th number)

d 42 pins (the most frequent number, 6 boxes)

Number of pins	Number of boxes	pins × boxes
39	3	117
40	5	200
41	4	164
42	6	252
43	2	86

The stem-and-leaf diagram shows the temperatures, in °C, for 10 successive days.

Calculate **a** the mean

b the mode

c the median

d the range of the temperatures.

1	1 2 6 6 7
2	1 2 4 5
3	1

Key: | 1 | 1 | means 11 °C

a Mean $= (11 + 12 + 16 + 16 + 17 + 21 + 22 + 24 + 25 + 31) \div 10$

$= 195 \div 10 = 19.5$ °C

b Mode $= 16$ °C (the most frequent temperature)

c Median $= (17 + 21) \div 2 = 19$ °C (using the 5th and 6th temperatures)

d Range $= 31 - 11 = 20$ °C (highest temperature minus lowest temperature)

The numbers of leaves are counted on 20 plants.

The results are shown in the frequency table.

a Calculate an estimate of the mean.

b State the modal class.

Number of leaves	Number of plants
1–5	6
6–10	4
11–15	8
16–20	2

a Estimated mean

$= (18 + 32 + 104 + 36) \div 20$

$= 190 \div 20$

$= 9.5$ leaves

b Modal class = 11–15 (the most frequent class)

Number of leaves	Number of plants	Mid-value	Mid × plants
1–5	6	3	18
6–10	4	8	32
11–15	8	13	104
16–20	2	18	36

Exercise D4

 1 The attendances at 5 football matches are shown.

Calculate

   a the mean

   b the median

   c the range of the attendances.

(F p230, 232, 234, F+ p230, 232)

35 464
34 984
33 894
33 879
34 084

2 The hours of sunshine for one day in November at 9 cities are shown in the ordered stem-and-leaf diagram.

   a Calculate the mean hours of sunshine.

   b Find the median hours of sunshine.

   c State the mode hours of sunshine.

   d Calculate the range of the hours of sunshine.

(F p272, F+ p270)

0	0 8 8
1	3 6
2	5 6
3	0 6

Key: | 0 | 8 | means 0.8 hours

3 The bar chart shows how often 18 students use their mobile phone in one day.

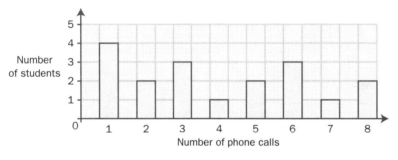

   a Calculate the total number of phone calls made by the 18 students.

   b Calculate the mean number of phone calls per student.

   c Calculate the range of the number of phone calls.

(F p234, 236, F+ p234)

 4 Jack delivers milk. He records the number of bottles he delivers at 25 houses.

   a Calculate the total number of milk bottles delivered to the 25 houses.

   b Calculate the mean number of milk bottles delivered per house.

   c State the mode number of bottles delivered.

   d Find the median number of bottles delivered.

   e Calculate the range of the number of bottles delivered.

(F p236, F+ p234)

Number of pints	Number of houses
0	0
1	8
2	5
3	7
4	5

5 Twenty sacks of potatoes are weighed to the nearest kilogram.

a Calculate the total weight of all the sacks of potatoes.

b Calculate the mean weight per sack.

c State the mode weight.

d Find the median weight.

e Calculate the range of the weights.

(F p236, F+ p234)

Weight (kg)	Number of sacks
15	2
16	4
17	3
18	6
19	5

6 The number of tents on a campsite is recorded each day for a month.

a State the possible months when the survey took place.

b State the modal class.

c Which class interval contains the median?

d Calculate an estimate of the mean.

(F+ p238)

Number of tents	Frequency
0–2	16
3–5	6
6–8	3
9–11	5

Use the mid-values of each class interval.

7 Chloe made a list of her homework marks.

a Write down the mode of her homework marks.

b Work out her mean homework mark.

(*Edexcel Ltd., 2005*) 3 marks

Homework Marks
4, 5, 5, 5, 4, 3, 2, 1, 4, 5

8 The table shows information about the number of hours that 120 children used a computer last week.

Work out an estimate for the mean number of hours that the children used a computer. Give your answer correct to two decimal places.

(*Edexcel Ltd., 2005*) 4 marks

Number of hours (h)	Frequency
$0 < h \leq 2$	10
$2 < h \leq 4$	15
$4 < h \leq 6$	30
$6 < h \leq 8$	35
$8 < h \leq 10$	25
$10 < h \leq 12$	5

- You can compare two sets of numerical data using
  — a measure of **spread**: the range
  — a measure of **average**: the mean
  the mode or modal class
  the median

See D4 for range, mean, mode, modal class and median.

- You can compare two sets of data using graphs.
  A **comparative bar chart** combines two bar charts.

  Bar chart to show Belinda's and Alan's exam results

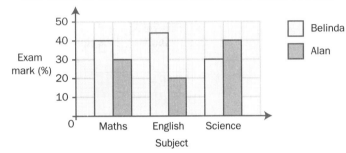

Belinda did better than Alan in Maths and English.

Alan did better than Belinda in Science.

- Two **frequency polygons** of related data can be shown on the same graph.

  Graph to show the ages of
  people in groups A and B

See D3 for frequency polygons.

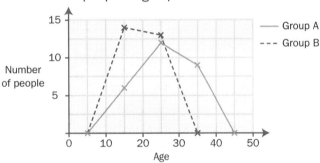

Group A has a larger range.

Group B has a lower modal class.

- You use a **line graph** to show how data changes with time.

  The number of late buses is shown for each successive year.

  Graph to show the number of buses that were late

Time series graphs are not frequency polygons.

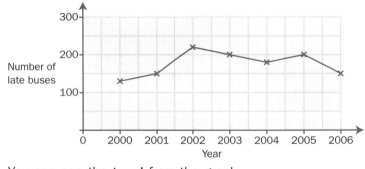

Time is always the horizontal axis.

You can see the **trend** from the graph.

- Two line graphs of related time series data can be shown on the same graph.

  You can compare the attendances for a particular day during the week.

Graph to show the attendance
of Classes A and B

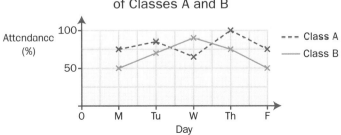

Example

The frequency polygons show the amount spent by customers at two supermarkets.

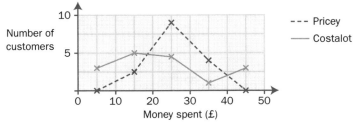

Make two statements to compare the amount spent at the two supermarkets.

Both Pricey's and Costalot's customers spent between £5 and £45.

The modal class at Pricey is £20 to £30, but the modal class at Costalot is £10 to £20.

(Most customers at Pricey paid between £20 and £30, but most customers at Costalot paid between £10 and £20.)

One statement about the range. ◄──►

One statement about the modal class. ↕

Example

An exam consists of Paper 1 and Paper 2.

The mean and range for Paper 1 are shown.

Paper 1	
Mean	35%
Range	55%

The marks for Paper 2 were

45%   36%   56%   64%   60%

75%   80%   72%   63%   59%

a Calculate the mean and range of the Paper 2 marks.

b Make two statements to compare the Paper 1 and Paper 2 marks.

See D4 for mean and range.

a mean = (45 + 36 + 56 + 64 + 60 + 75 + 80 + 72 + 63 + 59) ÷ 10

= 610 ÷ 10 = 61%

range = 80 − 36 = 44%

b On average, the Paper 1 marks are lower than the Paper 2 marks.

The Paper 1 marks are more spread out than the Paper 2 marks.

Using the mean.

Using the range.

Example

The line graphs show the amount of newspaper and glass that is recycled as a percentage of all rubbish.

Describe the trend for recycled newspaper and glass.

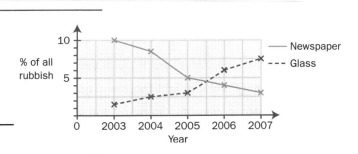

The percentage of recycled newspapers is decreasing year by year.

The percentage of recycled glass is increasing year by year.

Exercise D5

1 Grace and Matt deliver newspapers.

The comparative bar chart shows the number they deliver one weekend.

a Calculate the total number of newspapers delivered by Matt.

Grace and Matt are paid 5p for each newspaper they deliver.

b Calculate the amount of money Grace and Matt should receive.

(F p268, F+ p268)

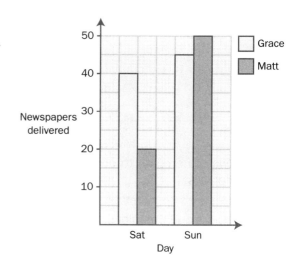

2 The stem-and-leaf diagram shows the number of people who watched the school girls' football team play this season.

a Calculate the mean and range of this data.

The mean and range are calculated for the attendances at the boys' football team matches.

b Make **two** statements to compare the attendances for each team.

(F p238, 272, F+ p236, 270)

0	5
1	3 6 7 9
2	0 4 4 8 8

Key: | 1 | 3 | means 13 people

Mean	8
Range	3

3 Peter and Abi attend a weight-loss club.

The line graphs show their progress over 10 weeks.

This is a time-series graph.

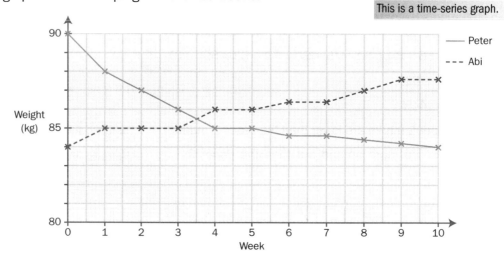

a State the starting weights of Peter and Abi.

b Calculate Abi's overall weight gain over the 10 weeks.

c When was Peter's weight the same as Abi's weight?

The weight-loss club offer to return the joining fee, if you lose 10% of your starting weight over 10 weeks.

$10\% = \frac{1}{10}$

d Does Peter qualify for his money back? Show your working.

(F p274, F+ p272)

4 Nathan lives in a street **with** speed humps.

Judy lives in a street **without** speed humps.

The frequency polygons show the number of cars and their speeds in the two streets.

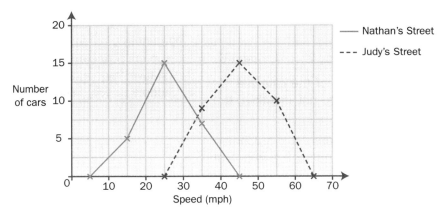

a Make one statement to compare the spread of the car speeds in each street.

b Make one statement to compare the average speed of the cars in each street.

(F+ p268)

5 A shop has a sale.

The bar chart shows some information about the sale.

The normal price of a vacuum cleaner is £80.

The sale price of a vacuum cleaner is £60.

The price of a vacuum cleaner is reduced from £80 to £60.

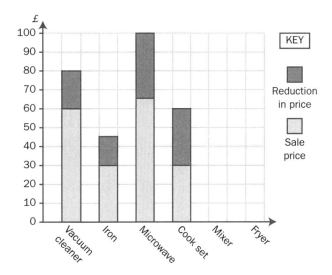

a Write the sale price of a vacuum cleaner as a fraction of its normal price. Give your answer in its simplest form.

b Find the reduction in the price of the iron.

c Which **two** items have the same sale price?

d Which item has the greatest reduction in price?

Mixer	
Normal price	£90
Sale price	£70

Fryer	
Normal price	£85
Sale price	£70

e Copy and complete the bar chart for the mixer and the fryer.

(*Edexcel Ltd., 2004*) 7 marks

D6 Probability

- A **trial** is an activity.

  Rolling a dice is a trial.

- An **outcome** is one possible result of a trial.

  The outcomes of rolling an ordinary dice are 1, 2, 3, 4, 5 and 6.

  Each outcome is **equally likely** as the faces of the dice are identical in size and shape. If the faces were not identical, the dice would be **biased**.

  These outcomes are **mutually exclusive** because the outcomes cannot occur at the same time. You cannot roll a 3 and a 4 at the same time.

- An **event** is one or more outcomes of a trial.

  An even number is an event when rolling an ordinary dice.

- Probability measures the chance of an event happening.

  All probabilities have a value between 0 and 1 and can be marked on a **probability scale**.

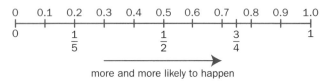

more and more likely to happen

  Probability of an event happening = $\dfrac{\text{Number of favourable outcomes}}{\text{Total number of all possible outcomes}}$

- The probabilities of mutually exclusive outcomes add up to 1.

  Probability of an event **not** happening = 1 − probability of an event happening

- The **expected frequency** is the number of times you expect the event to happen.

  Expected frequency = probability × number of trials

- You can estimate the probability from experiments.
  The estimated or experimental probability is called the **relative frequency**.

  Relative frequency = $\dfrac{\text{Number of successful trials}}{\text{Total number of trials}}$

  The estimated probability is more reliable the greater the number of trials.

- You need to show the outcomes of two successive events in a systematic way.

  You could use a **sample space diagram**.

0 means impossible
$\frac{1}{2}$ means even chance
1 means certain

For a dice $P(4) = \frac{1}{6}$

For a dice $P(\text{not } 4) = 1 - P(4)$

See the example.

Example

The adults and children at a multi-cinema complex are counted one evening.

The results are shown in the two-way table.

	Cinema 1	Cinema 2	Total
Adults	26	9	35
Children	8	7	15
Total	34	16	50

One of the cinema-goers is chosen at random.

Calculate the probability that the person is

a a child   **b** in Cinema 2.

a P(a child) $=\dfrac{15}{50}=\dfrac{3}{10}$ **b** P(in Cinema 2) $=\dfrac{16}{50}=\dfrac{8}{25}$

Example

The probability that a spinner lands on red is 0.2.

Claire spins the spinner once.

a Calculate the probability that the spinner does **not** land on red.

The spinner is spun for a total of 50 times.

b Calculate the number of times you would expect the spinner to **not** land on red.

a P(not red) $= 1 - $ P(red) $= 1 - 0.2 = 0.8$

b $0.8 \times 50 = 40$ times

Example

A coin has a Head (H) or a Tail (T).

A dice is numbered 1, 2, 3 and 4.

Fiona spins the coin and rolls the dice.

a List all the possible outcomes.

b Calculate the probability of a Head and an even number.

a Three ways to systematically show the outcomes are shown.

Coin	H	T	H	T	H	T	H	T
Dice	1	1	2	2	3	3	4	4

Head 1, Tail 1, Head 2, Tail 2, Head 3, Tail 3, Head 4, Tail 4

		Dice			
		1	**2**	**3**	**4**
Coin	**Head**	(H,1)	(H,2)	(H,3)	(H,4)
	Tail	(T,1)	(T,2)	(T,3)	(T,4)

This is a **sample space diagram**.

b P(Head and even number) $=\dfrac{\text{Number of favourable outcomes}}{\text{Total number of all possible outcomes}}$

$$=\dfrac{2}{8}=\dfrac{1}{4}$$

Exercise D6

1 Cards marked 1 to 20 are placed face down.

One card is selected at random.

Calculate the probability that the card is

a the number 13

b an even number

c a multiple of 4

See N1 for multiple and factor.

d a factor of 24

e a square number.

See N5 for square number.

(F p140, F+ p134)

2 A spinner consists of four different colours:
Blue, Green, Red and Yellow.

The angles of the sectors are shown.

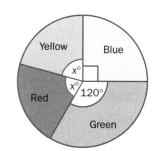

Colour	Blue	Green	Red	Yellow
Angle	$90°$	$120°$	$x°$	$x°$

a Calculate the value of x.

b Calculate the probability of spinning

  i Blue   **ii** Green

  iii Red   **iv** Yellow.

c If the spinner is spun 120 times, how many times would you expect it to land on Blue?

(F p330, F+ p140)

3 A dice is rolled 60 times.

The frequency table shows the results.

Score	Frequency
1	8
2	11
3	10
4	9
5	12
6	10

a State the modal score.

b Use the relative frequency of each score to estimate the probability of scoring

  i a 1   **ii** a 2   **iii** a 3   **iv** a 4   **v** a 5   **vi** a 6.

c Explain how the relative frequencies can be made more reliable.

(F p332, F+ p142)

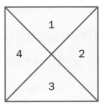

4 A red spinner is numbered 1 to 5 and a blue spinner is numbered 1 to 4.

Both spinners are spun. The scores on the spinners are added.

a List the 20 outcomes.

b What is the most likely total of the two spinners?

c Calculate the probability that the total is 5.

Give your answer as a cancelled fraction in its simplest form.

(F p334, F+ p334)

5 Some bulbs were planted in October.

The ticks in the table show the months in which each type of bulb grows into flowers.

		Month					
		Jan	Feb	March	April	May	June
Type of bulb	Allium					✓	✓
	Crocus	✓	✓				
	Daffodil		✓	✓	✓		
	Iris	✓	✓				
	Tulip				✓	✓	

a In which months do tulips flower?

b Which type of bulb flowers in March?

c In which month do most types of bulb flower?

d Which type of bulb flowers in the same months as the iris?

Ben puts one of each type of these bulbs in a bag.

He takes a bulb from the bag without looking.

e i Write down the probability that he will take a crocus bulb.

ii Draw a probability scale and mark with a cross (×) the probability that he will take a bulb which flowers in February.

(*Edexcel Ltd., 2005*) 6 marks

6 Mr Brown chooses one book from the library each week.

He chooses a crime novel or a horror story or a non-fiction book.

The probability that he chooses a horror story is 0.4.

The probability that he chooses a non-fiction book is 0.15.

Work out the probability that Mr Brown chooses a crime novel.

(*Edexcel Ltd., 2005*) 2 marks

Foundation Practice Exam Paper

100 marks total.

Time: 1 hour and 30 minutes

You may use a calculator.

1 Here is a list of 10 numbers.

1	2	4	5	7	9	16	24	30	36

From the list, write:

a A square number 16

b A multiple of 8 24

c All factors of 72. 1, 72   (4 marks)

2 a Measure the length of the line AB accurately.

A _____ B

b Draw a line of length 53 mm.   (2 marks)

$$\begin{array}{r} 591 \\ 6\,0\,0 \\ -\,2\,1\,7 \\ \hline 3\,8\,3 \end{array}$$

3 a Work out 600 − 217. 383

b Work out 3.2^2.   (4 marks)

4 a Draw a circle with radius 3 cm.

   i On your circle mark a point P on the circumference.

   ii Draw a diameter of the circle.

b

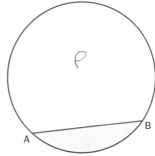

sector, radius, chord, diameter, segment, semicircle, arc, circumference.

From the list of words, choose the correct word to copy and complete these sentences.

   i AB is a ...diameter... of the circle.

   ii The shaded area is a ...radius... of the circle.   (4 marks)

5 Holly puts her 1p and 2p coins into a jar for a charity. For two weeks
she records how many coins she puts in each day.

0	2	3	0	2	6	4
4	5	5	2	1	1	6

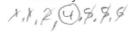

a Find the range of the number of coins Holly puts in each day. 6 − 1 = 5

b Find the mode of the number of coins Holly puts in each day. 5

c Find the median of the number of coins Holly puts in each day. 4

d In the two weeks Holly had put in 41 coins. The value of the coins was 59p.

How many 2p coins had she put in?   (5 marks)

6 A typist uses the formula

Cost = 2 × number of pages + 6

to work out how much she will charge (in £s) a student to type up their dissertation.

Coralie's dissertation is 47 pages long. How much will the typist charge her? *(2 marks)*

7 a Estimate 69.3 × 3.1.
Show your working.

b 30 square tiles are to be arranged in the shape of a rectangle. One possible way is a rectangle with length 15 and width 2.

Write the length and width of **two** other ways. *(4 marks)*

8 Beth and Louise are playing dressing up games. They have to choose a skirt colour from red, green or blue and a colour of top from black, red or white.

List all the possible colour combinations they can have. *(2 marks)*

9 A recipe book says that a joint of beef should be cooked for 70 minutes per kg plus 40 minutes.

a Dave wants to cook a 1.6 kg joint of beef. How many minutes does he need to cook it for?

b Give your answer in hours and minutes. *(4 marks)*

10 a Calculate the cube of 5.

b Calculate 3^4. *(2 marks)*

11 Molly buys 0.6 kg Cheddar and 0.3 kg Camembert for £5.22. Cheddar costs £5.40 per kg. How much does Camembert cost? *(4 marks)*

12 a Write the next term in the sequence   2,   4,   7,   11,   16

b Describe in words the rule for working out the next term.

c The 19th term is 191. What will the 20th term be? *(3 marks)*

13 The graph shows some information about the temperature in °C in Leeds one day in April.

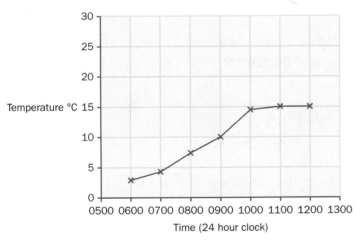

a What was the temperature at 7 am?

b How much warmer was it at 12 noon than at 7 am?

c Molly says that the temperature is going to rise above 20°C during the afternoon. Explain why it is unlikely that Molly will be right. *(4 marks)*

14 The timetable shows the buses Ramesh can catch from his home in Marlow to work in Shiplake.

High Wycombe	0630	0700	0730
Marlow	0649	0722	0753
Medmenham	0656	0730	0801
Henley	0705	0741	0815
Twyford	——	0751	——
Sonning	——	0753	——
Shiplake	0719	——	0819

$\pi = \dfrac{22}{7}$

a Ramesh catches the bus at 0753. How long should the journey to Shiplake take him?

b There is an accident which means the bus is 22 minutes late arriving at Shiplake. What time does Ramesh arrive in Shiplake? *(2 marks)*

15

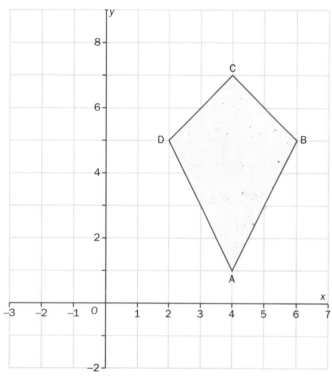

a ABCD is a kite. Work out the area of the kite.

b M is the midpoint of AD. Give the coordinates of the point M. *(3 marks)*

16 **a** Divide £160 in the ratio 3 : 1.

b Work out $\dfrac{2}{5} \div 4$. Give your answer in its simplest form. *(4 marks)*

17 **a** Factorise $6x^3 + 18x$.

b Expand and simplify $3(x + 4) - 2(x + 1)$.

c Solve $5x - 2 = 6 + 3x$. *(7 marks)*

18 In this question use $\pi = \frac{22}{7}$.

A circle has diameter 12 cm.

Calculate the area of the circle. *(4 marks)*

19 **a** Copy and complete the table for $y = x^2 - 2x + 1$.

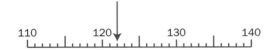

x	−1	0	1	2	3
y		1	0		4

b Plot the graph of $y = x^2 - 3x + 1$ on a suitable grid. *(4 marks)*

20 **a** Write down the reading on the scale.

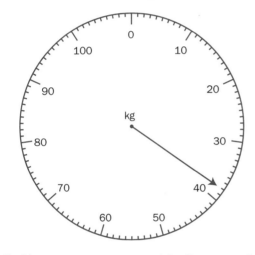

b i Write down the reading on the scale.

ii Give your answer correct to the nearest 10 kg. *(3 marks)*

21

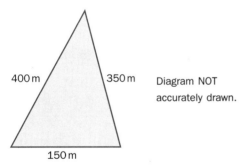

400 m   350 m   Diagram NOT
                   accurately drawn.

150 m

Make an accurate scale drawing of the triangle in the sketch.
Use a scale of 1 cm to 50 m. *(3 marks)*

22 **a** Work out $2.5^2 + \sqrt{5.7}$. Write down all the digits on your calculator.

b Round your answer correct to 2 decimal places. *(2 marks)*

23

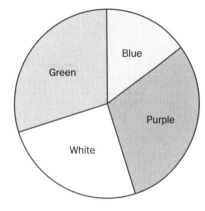

A spinner is shown.
The probability the spinner lands on blue is 0.15, and the probability it lands on white is 0.25.
Purple and green are equally likely.

a Work out the probability that the spinner lands on green.

b The spinner is spun 450 times. How many times would you expect it to land on green?

(4 marks)

24

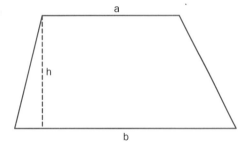

The area, A, of a trapezium is given by the formula. $A = \left(\dfrac{a+b}{2}\right) \times h$

Calculate the area when $a = 4$, $b = 7$ and $h = 6$.

(3 marks)

25 The price of a car is increased from £7350 to £7550. Calculate the percentage increase, correct to 1 decimal place.

(3 marks)

26 **a** Solve $7x - 5 = 23$

b Solve $2x + 1 = 6x + 9$

(5 marks)

27 Marlon has a biased die. He throws it 75 times, and the results are shown in the table.

Score	Frequency	
1	1	
2	5	
3	5	
4	3	
5	9	
6	52	

Calculate the mean score.

(3 marks)

28 The diagram shows a prism whose cross section is a right-angled triangle.
The prism is 14 cm long.
Its base is 3 cm wide and the sloping edge of the prism is 6 cm long.
Calculate the volume of the prism.
Give your answer correct to 3 significant figures. *(6 marks)*

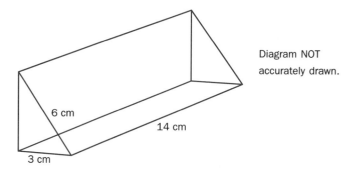

Diagram NOT
accurately drawn.

Answers

Exercise N1

1 a 467
  b 15 208
  c 5044

2 a 30
  b 5
  c 200
  d 4000

3 345, 354, 435, 453, 534, 543

4 a Both use 12, 24, 36, …, 192
  b Gillian 49, Chris 66, both 16
  c Gillian

5 a 11
  b 18
  c 10, 15
  d Because you cannot multiply 30 by an integer and get 10 or 15. 10 and 15 are factors of 30, not multiples.

6 a 1, 2, 3, 4, 6, 12
  b 1, 3, 5, 9, 15, 45
  c 1, 3

7 a 10, 20, 30, 40, 50, 60
  b 15, 30, 45, 60, 75, 90
  c 30, 60

8 a 300
  b 480
  c 5000

9 550

10 a 1, 2, 4, 7, 14, 28
      1, 2, 3, 6, 7, 14, 21, 42
   b 1, 2, 7, 14
   c 14

11 a 6, 12, 18, 24, 30
      9, 18, 27, 36, 45
   b 18

12 a 17 252
   b 5400
   c 4000

13 a i 1459
     ii 9541
   b 5 + 9 = 14
   c 0

Exercise N2

1 a A 9 square grid with any 3 squares shaded
  b $\frac{2}{3}$

2 a $\frac{5}{100}$
  b $\frac{6}{10}$
  c $\frac{4}{1000}$

3 a 4.58, 4.6, 4.66, 4.7
  b 30.1, 30.15, 30.19, 30.2
  c 8.45, 8.455, 8.5, 8.55

4 a $\frac{3}{5}$, 60%
  b $\frac{1}{20}$, 5%
  c $\frac{3}{20}$, 15%
  d $\frac{1}{8}$, 12.5%

5 a $\frac{2}{5}$, 0.4
  b $\frac{7}{10}$, 0.7
  c $\frac{13}{20}$, 0.65
  d $\frac{12}{25}$, 0.48

6 a 70%, 0.7
  b 54%, 0.54
  c 30%, 0.3
  d 65%, 0.65

7

	Cancelled fraction	Decimal	Percentage
a	$\frac{1}{2}$	0.5	50%
b	$\frac{1}{5}$	0.2	20%
c	$\frac{3}{10}$	0.3	30%
d	$\frac{3}{4}$	0.75	75%
e	$\frac{9}{10}$	0.9	90%

8 a $0.\dot{2}$
  b $0.1\dot{6}$
  c $0.\dot{1}4285\dot{7}$

9 a $\frac{4}{5}$
  b 80%

10 a $\frac{15}{24}, \frac{16}{24}, \frac{21}{24}, \frac{18}{24}, \frac{12}{24}$
   b $\frac{1}{2}, \frac{5}{8}, \frac{2}{3}, \frac{3}{4}, \frac{7}{8}$

11 a $\frac{2}{5}$, 43%, $\frac{22}{50}$, 0.48

   b $\frac{4}{5}$, 83%, 0.85, 0.9

   c 0.17, $\frac{1}{5}$, 22%, $\frac{1}{4}$

12 a $\frac{2}{5}$

   b 0.98

   c 7 500 000

   d 25%

   e 60%

13 $\frac{2}{3}$ $\left(\text{because } \frac{2}{3} = \frac{10}{15} \text{ whereas } \frac{3}{5} = \frac{9}{15}\right)$

Exercise N3

1 1262

2 a 784
   b 20 090
   c 45

3 a −7
   b 14
   c −2

4 a −40
   b −8
   c 6

5 a $\frac{23}{24}$

   b $\frac{2}{3}$

   c $1\frac{2}{9}$

6 a $\frac{1}{6}$

   b 3
   c 36

7 a 15 m
   b 105 m

8 a $\frac{2}{3}$

   b $2\frac{1}{4}$

   c 32

9 a 10
   b 8
   c 100

10 a Rob is keying 160 ÷ 80, then adding 20.
   b 1.6

11 192 miles

12 a 1 m, $\frac{1}{25}$ m^2

   b $3\frac{1}{20}$ feet, $\frac{9}{20}$ feet^2

   c $3\frac{1}{5}$ cm, $\frac{16}{25}$ cm^2

13 a $\frac{1}{12}$

   b 140

14 a 90°C
   b 540°C
   c Jupiter
   d −230°C

Exercise N4

1 a 14
   b 9
   c £17.22

2 a 17.56
   b 6
   c 0.5

3 £0.63

4 a 39.470 951 89
   b 40

5 a 18
   b 3.6
   c 8.4
   d 20
   e 3.75

6 a 1400
   b 25
   c 6

7 £148.75

8 a 66.4
   b 0.09
   c 2.04
   d 9.8
   e 15
   f 5.6

9 6.3

10 a 34.3 km
   b 1784 km

11 a 128.8
   b 2.3

12 10

13 a £458.40
   b £14.50

14 £77.74 since whole litres purchased.

Exercise N5

1 Any 3 × 3 square
   Any 4 × 4 square

2 a 16, 27, 32, 25
   b 4^2, 5^2, 3^3, 2^5

3 97 336

4 a 9

  b 9^2

  c 3^4

5 a i 8

    ii 1

    iii 1000

  b i 4

    ii 1

    iii 100

6 a $4^2 + 1^2$

  b $5^2 + 2^2$

  c $5^2 + 4^2$

  d $8^2 + 7^2$

7 6 cm

8 a 40

  b 200

  c 144

  d 900

9 a 0.5

  b 0.25

  c 0.04

  d 0.02

10 a 10^5

  b 10^4

  c 10^7

  d 10

11 2 and 3

12 a $2 \times 3 \times 5$

  b $2^3 \times 5$

  c 10

  d 120

13 a $2^2 \times 3^2$

  b $2 \times 3^2 \times 5$

  c 18

  d 180

14 a 3^{10}

  b 3^3

  c 3^3

15 a i 25

    ii 28

    iii 5 and 20

    iv 26 and 33

  b because $2^3 = 2 \times 2 \times 2 = 8$

Exercise N6

1 Japan by 1110 YEN (or £5)

2 a £45.60

  b 12.5

  c 36 hours

3 200 ml

4 a 2 km

  b 30 cm

5 a 72 km

  b 75 miles

  c 5 mph

6 Becca £175, Carly £50, Donna £125

7 a 2 : 1

  b 200 g wholemeal, 100 g plain

8 8 m/s

9 a £2.40

  b £2

  c €1.25

10 62.5 cm

11 £12.60

12 a 200 g

  b 600 ml

Exercise N7

1

Percentage of £60	Amount
10%	£6
5%	£3
2.5%	£1.50
17.5%	£10.50

2 80% of £315 = £252

  75% of £332 = £249

  60% of £410 = £246

3 540 g

4 a £8.40

  b £8.40

5 a £42

  b £828

  c £30

6 a 1.05

  b 5%

7 a £1.50

  b 6%

8 £540.80

9 a 8 days

  b £75.20

  c £128.52

10 £9720

Exercise N8

1 a 450

  b 300

  c 180.5

  d 0.075

  e 8.13

  f 0.006

2 a Because 8.67 ÷ 10 is smaller than 8.67

  b 0.867

3

Power of 10	Meaning	Number
10^3	$10 \times 10 \times 10$	1000
10^4	$10 \times 10 \times 10 \times 10$	10 000
10^5	$10 \times 10 \times 10 \times 10 \times 10$	100 000
10^6	$10 \times 10 \times 10 \times 10 \times 10 \times 10$	1 000 000

4 a 3900
 b 48.5
 c 320 000
 d 4.3
 e 0.038
 f 0.031

5 a 42 is not between 1 and 10.
 b The power of 10 is not an integer.
 c 8.9 is not multiplied by a power of 10.

6 a 4.8×10^3
 b 9.62×10^5
 c 5.67×10^2
 d 3.21×10^4
 e 7.5×10^6
 f 3×10^7

7 a 2.5×10^6
 b 223 000 000

8 a 1 500 000, 1 050 000, 980 000, 890 000
 b 8.9×10^5, 9.8×10^5, 1.05×10^6, 1.5×10^6

9 a 279 000 000
 b 2.79×10^8

10 $1.148 08 \times 10^{11}$

11 a Athens
 b 343 km
 c Rome
 d Paris
 e Paris

12 a 7.2×10^8
 b 5×10^2
 c 6.012×10^5

13 1.4×10^{10}

Exercise A1
1 a $n - 3$
 b £2b
 c $\frac{3}{4}h$

2 $A = n + 1$
 $B = n + 10$
 $C = n - 1$

3 36a

4 60y pence

5 $5p + 10q$ pence

6 a 6
 b 12
 c 48
 d −4
 e −2

7 a either
 b even
 c either
 d either
 e odd

8 The two expressions are $2(y + y)$ and $2y + 2y$.

9 a $2p + 3q$
 b $y(3y - 1)$
 c $3c + 4d$
 d $8pq$

Exercise A2
1 a h^4
 b m^2
 c p

2 a $a(a + 5)\,cm^2$
 b $a^2 + 5a\,cm^2$

3 $2(x - 3) = 2x - 6$
 $x(x - 3) = x^2 - 3x$
 $2x^2 - 3x = x(2x - 3)$
 $3(x - 2) = 3x - 6$

4 a $4(2x - 3)$
 b $x(x + 4)$
 c $3m(1 + 4m)$

5 a s^9
 b s^4
 c s^7
 d $10s^4$
 e $8s^3$

6 a $x^2 + 5x + 6$
 b $x^2 + x - 6$
 c $x^2 - 2x - 8$
 d $x^2 - 7x + 12$
 e $x^2 + 4x + 4$

7 a $x^2 + 2xy + y^2$
 b 100

8 a $x^2 - 1$
 b 9800

9 a p^9
 b $6q^6$

10 a $x^2 + 3x - 28$
 b $y^4 + 2y^2$
 c $p(p + 6)$
 d $3x(2x - 3y)$

Exercise A3

1 a $5x + 13 = 48$
  b 7

2 a $3n + 8$, $5n + 8$
  b $8n + 16 = 48$
  c 4
  d 12, 8, 20

3 a $4x + 5 = 13$
  b £2

4 a $5(n - 3) = 45$
  b 12

5 a $5d + 5 = 25$
  b $d = 4$
    Sides are 4, 4, 5, 5 and 7 cm.

6 a $x = 6$
  b $a = 7$
  c $b = 6$
  d $x = 4$
  e $x = \pm 3$
  f $x = 2$
  g $x = 6$

7 $r = -11$

8 $142°$

Exercise A4

1 500 m

2 a Mark has made $6^2 = 6 \times 2$ instead of 6×6
  b $36\pi\,cm^2$

3 a 18

4 a 120 mins or 2 hours
  b 4 kg

5 $T = 3n + 5$

6 a $d = 5(p + 1)$
  b $d = 5p + 5$

7 $a = \dfrac{180 - b}{2}$

8 $d = \dfrac{C}{\pi}$

9 $C = 10(n + 3)$

10 a $-1\frac{1}{2}$
  b $t = \dfrac{v - u}{5}$

Exercise A5

1 a 10
  b 20
  c 100

2 a 26, 32
  b The terms start at 2 and increase by 6 each time so they are all even numbers.

3 a 1, 3, 6, 10
  b 15
  c triangular numbers

4 A counter-example is $5 \times 3 = 15$ which is an odd number.

5 2 is a prime number and is even.

6 $7n + 1$

7 a 5, 8, 11, 14
  b $3n + 2$
  c There is a central rectangle of $3n$ dots and then one extra dot to each side.
  d Number of dots = $3 \times$ the pattern number + 2
  e 62

8 $5n + 1$

9 a $\dfrac{4 \times 5}{2}$
  b $1 + 2 + 3 + 4 + 5 + 6 + 7 + 8 = \dfrac{8 \times 9}{2}$
  c 5050
  d $\dfrac{n(n + 1)}{2}$

Exercise A6

1 a B
  b A
  c D
  d C

2 a −1, 0, 1
  b 1, 2, 3
  c −2, −1, 0

3 a $x \geqslant 4$
  b $x > 3\frac{1}{2}$
  c $x \leqslant -2$
  d $y > 3$
  e $x > 2$

4 $2 < y < 6$

5

x	x^2	$x^2 + 2x$	too big or too small
3	9	15	too small
4	16	24	too big
3.5	12.25	19.25	too small
3.6	12.96	20.16	too big
3.55	12.6025	19.7025	too small

Therefore solution lies between 3.55 and 3.6, so $x = 3.6$ (1 dp).

6 5.4 cm

7

x	x^3	$x^3 + x$	too big or too small
2	8	10	too small
3	27	30	too big
2.5	15.625	18.125	too small
2.7	19.683	22.383	too small
2.8	21.952	24.752	too big
2.75	20.796875	23.546875	too small

Therefore solution lies between 2.75 and 2.8, so $x = 2.8$ (1 dp).

8 5.6 secs

9 a $x = 0.6$
b −3, −2, −1, 0, 1, 2

10

x	x^3	$x^3 - 4x$	too big or too small
3	27	15	too small
4	64	48	too big
3.5	42.875	28.875	too big
3.4	39.304	25.704	too big
3.3	35.937	22.737	too small
3.35	37.595375	24.195375	too big

Therefore solution lies between 3.3 and 3.35, so $x = 3.3$ (1 dp).

Exercise A7

1 a

x	−2	−1	0	1	2
y	−5	−3	−1	1	3

b

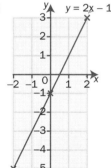

c i 2
ii −1.5

2 a

x	−1	0	1	2	3	4
y	4	3	2	1	0	−1

b

x	−1	0	1	2
y	−0.5	1.5	3.5	5.5

c

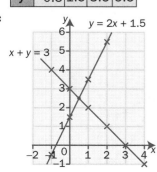

d (0.5, 2.5)

3 a B
b C
c D
d A

4 Any line of the form $y = 4x + c$ where $c \neq 3$

5 a

x	−3	−2	−1	0	1	2	3
y	9	4	1	0	1	4	9

b, c

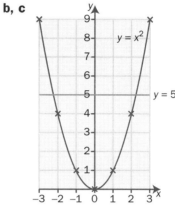

d $x = \pm 2.2$

6 a

x	−1	0	1	2	3
y	6	5	4	3	2

b

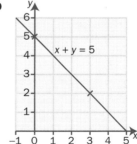

7 a 8
b Any line of the form $y = \frac{1}{2}x + c$ where $c \neq 1$
c $x = 2(y - 1)$

Exercise A8

1 a 30 ft
b 4.5 m
c 25 ft

2 a Second floor
b 5 secs
c They are the same.

3 a D
b E
c B
d A
e C

4 a

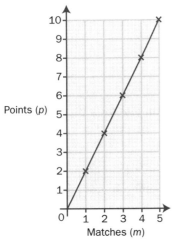

Points (*p*) — vertical axis, Matches (*m*) — horizontal axis

b $p = 2m$

5 a

b

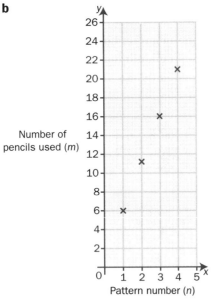

Number of pencils used (*m*) — vertical axis
Pattern number (*n*) — horizontal axis

c 51

d $m = 5n + 1$

Exercise S1

1 a obtuse angle
b right angle
c reflex angle
d acute angle

2 The angles of the triangle should add up to 180°, not 170°.

3 a 73°
b 169°

4 140°, 110°, 60°, 50°

5 $a = 57°$, $b = 30°$, $c = 93°$

6 a 060°
b 240°

7 a i 143°
ii an obtuse angle

b

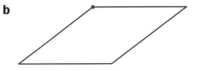

8 a 60°
b 120°
c 12 cm^2

Exercise S2

1

square	yes
rectangle	no
isosceles trapezium	no
parallelogram	no
rhombus	yes

2 D(2, −1)

3 a 72°, isosceles
b 90°, right-angled
c 95°, scalene
d 60°, equilateral
e 45°, right-angled

4 a octagon

b

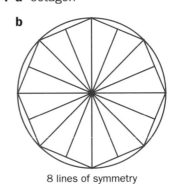

8 lines of symmetry

c 8

5

6 a

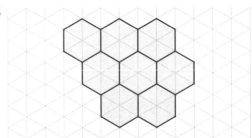

Two possible answers

b

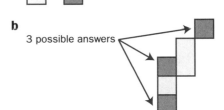

3 possible answers

Exercise S3

1 a triangular prism
  b sphere
  c hexagonal based pyramid
  d pentagonal prism
  e cone
  f cylinder
  g triangular based pyramid (tetrahedron)
  h square based pyramid

2 a C
  b $32\,\text{cm}^2$

3 a i 8
   ii 12
   iii 6
  b There are 5 possible answers:
The plane passing through the central square section
One of the 2 planes passing through the top and bottom vertices and a diagonal of the central square section
One of the 2 planes passing through the top and bottom vertices and through the mid-points of two opposite sides of the central square section

4

5 A (0,0,0), B (4,0,3), C (4,1,3)

6 a, b, c

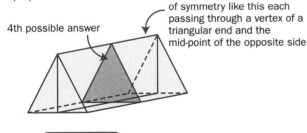

4th possible answer

There are 3 possible planes of symmetry like this each passing through a vertex of a triangular end and the mid-point of the opposite side

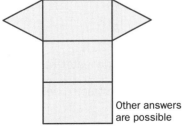

Other answers are possible

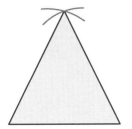

7 a, b

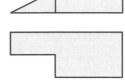

Exercise S4

1 a perimeter = 24 cm, area = $24\,\text{cm}^2$
  b i perimeter = 36 cm, area = $48\,\text{cm}^2$
   ii perimeter = 32 cm, area = $48\,\text{cm}^2$
   iii perimeter = 36 cm, area = $48\,\text{cm}^2$
   iv perimeter = 28 cm, area = $48\,\text{cm}^2$

2 $21.5\,\text{cm}^2$

3 a $108\,\text{cm}^2$
  b $72\,\text{cm}^3$

4 b

5 a $18\,\text{cm}^2$
  b $108\,\text{cm}^3$

6 a i $4\,\text{cm}^2$
  a ii $10\,\text{cm}$
  b $28\,\text{cm}^3$

7

Expression	Length	Area	Volume	None of these
$x + y + z$	✓			
xyz			✓	
$xy + yz + xz$		✓		

Exercise S5

1 a i $x = 1$
   ii $y = 1$
   iii $x = -1$
  b translation $\begin{pmatrix} 4 \\ 0 \end{pmatrix}$

2 A,B,D

3 a yes
  b reflection in the line $y = -x$

4 $\begin{pmatrix} 3 \\ 7 \end{pmatrix}$

5 a parallelogram
  b

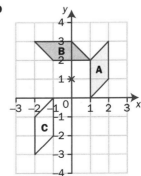

c either a 180° rotation about (0,0) or a translation $\begin{pmatrix} -3 \\ -3 \end{pmatrix}$

6 a

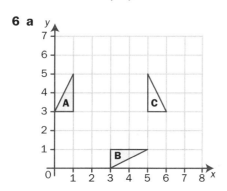

b reflection in the line $y = x$

7 a

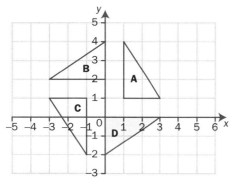

b a 180° rotation about (0,1)

Exercise S6

1 a right-angled triangle with base 6 cm and height 8 cm
  b 24 cm, 24 cm²

2 A as it is an enlargement scale factor 3.
  C as it is an enlargement scale factor 4.

3 a = 6 cm, b = 16 cm

4 a rhombus

  b

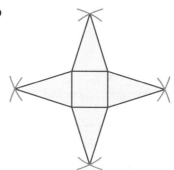

5 a Surface area = (1 × 2 + 2 × 3 + 1 × 3) × 2
    = 11 × 2 = 22 cm²
  b Volume = 1 × 2 × 3 = 6 cm³
  c 198 cm²
  d 162 cm³

6 image is a triangle with corners (−1,−4), (2,2), (−4,2)

7 160 ÷ 133 = 1.203...
  82 ÷ 72 = 1.138...
  Therefore the ratio of the lengths is not the same as the ratio of the widths, so the 2 rectangles cannot be similar.

Exercise S7

1 a This requires ruler and protractor only.
  b 6.2 cm

2 a square-based pyramid

  b

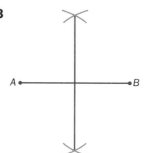

3

4

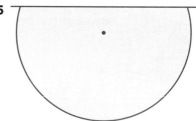

5

6 a i 065°
  a ii 315°
  b Shade a circle centre Manchester radius 3 cm.

7 a This requires ruler and protractor only.
  b 63°

Exercise S8

1

	metric	imperial
a	m	ft (or yards)
b	litres	gallons
c	g	oz
d	km	miles
e	kg	lb (or stones)

2 a 131.5°
  b 132.5°

3 Several answers are possible. A reasonable answer would be of the order:
  a 170 cm
  b 1.7 m
  c 5 m

4 a 1.5 mins
  b 75 kg
  c 8.54 cm

5 a 570 g
  b 1.5 cl
  c 1400 years

6 141 lb

7 12 m

8 (1,3)

9 a 5 g, 232 cm, 250 ml
  b 5 km

10 Yes, because 285 km per hour
  = 285 000 m per hour = 285 000 ÷ 3600 m/sec
  = 79.2 m/sec ≈ 80 m/sec

Exercise D1

1 a

Price of tickets	Tally	Frequency
£2	IIII I	6
£5	IIII IIII	9
£10	IIII IIII	9

  b 24
  c £147

2 a February

  b

Car mileage	Tally	Frequency
0 to 9	IIII I	6
10 to 19	IIII II	7
20 to 29	IIII I	6
30 to 39	IIII	5
40 to 49	IIII	4

  c 6 days

3 For each class, put all the names in a hat and draw one out.

4 The age groupings overlap, e.g. someone who is 20 could go in either of the first two groups. There is nowhere to record people over 60.

5 The categories 'Rarely' and 'Sometimes' are vague and not defined properly.

6 a 12
  b 40
  c 20%

7 a Many possible answers. An example is:
  Which of the following types of restaurant do you like to eat in?
      traditional English
      bistro
      fast food
      other (please specify)
  b He only asked members of his family.
  The question is a leading question suggesting that the answer expected is pizza. It also fails to ask people if there are other types of food they like apart from pizza and pasta.

8 a

Flavour of crisps	Tally	Frequency
Plain	IIII III	8
Chicken	III	3
Bovril	IIII	5
Salt & Vinegar	IIII	4

  b 4
  c Plain

Exercise D2

1

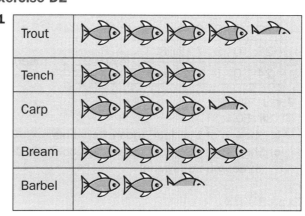

Trout	
Tench	
Carp	
Bream	
Barbel	

2 a

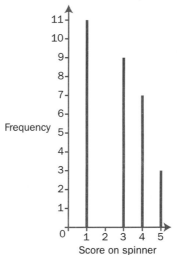

Line chart showing the scores obtained on a spinner.

  b Yes, biased against 2.

3 a 3°
  b Steve 210°, Charlie 60°, Jason 90°

c Pie chart showing the number of cars sold by 3 salesmen

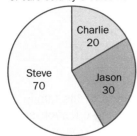

4

0	7 8 9
10	0 1 4 5 6 8
20	0 1 3 5 9
30	0 2 4 9
40	0 1

Key 10 | 5 means 15

5 Pie chart must have sector angles: Notebook 45°, Pens 135°, Magazines 180°.
You must give the pie chart a title and label the sectors.

6

20	3 4 8 9
21	2 5 7 7
22	0 6 8 9
23	0 3 7 8 8
24	0 1 1 2 5 6 8

Key 21 | 2 means 21.2 °C

7 a i 40
   ii 50
   b Show 5 of the 'four square' symbols
   c Show 2 of the 'four square' symbols and 1 'three square' symbol

Exercise D3

1 Bar chart showing the number of items in supermarket baskets

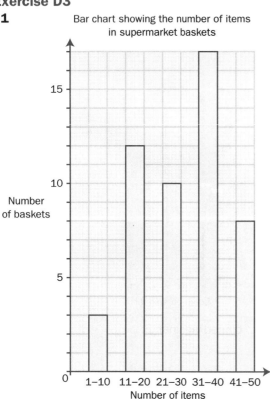

2

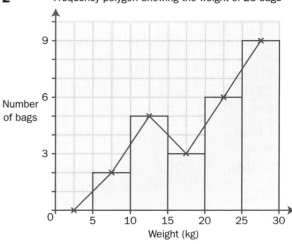

Frequency polygon showing the weight of 25 bags

3 a A none, B negative correlation, C positive correlation
   b A no, B yes, C yes
   c A no relationship, B students who spend more time on a computer spend less time reading books, C taller students weigh more

4 a

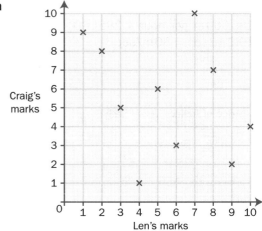

   b no correlation
   c no
   d In many cases, if Len gives a high mark, Craig gives a low mark and vice versa. However, they tend to agree for contestants C, D, and G.

5 a Histogram showing the distance walked by students in Jamal's class

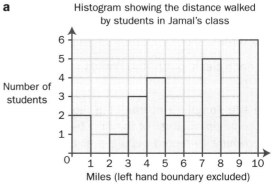

   b 10
   c 13
   d 25
   e 20%

6 a

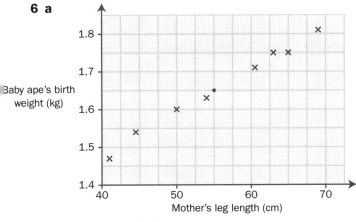

b positive correlation

c

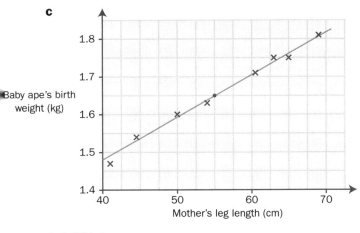

d 1.65 kg

Exercise D4

1 a 34 461
b 34 084
c 1585

2 a 1.8 hours
b 1.6 hours
c 0.8 hours
d 3.6 hours

3 a 72 hours
b 4 hours
c 7

4 a 59
b 2.36
c 1
d 2
e 3

5 a 348 kg
b 17.4 kg
c 18 kg
d 18 kg
e 4 kg

6 a April, June, September, November
b 0 – 2 tents
c 0 – 2 tents
d 3.7 tents

7 a 5
b 3.8

8 6.08 hours

Exercise D5

1 a 70
b Grace £4.25, Matt £3.50

2 a mean = 19.4, range = 23
b On average, the attendances at the girls' matches are higher than at the boys' matches (more than double). However, the spread of attendances at the boys' matches is much lower.

3 a Peter 90 kg, Abi 84 kg
b 3.5 kg
c after 3.6 weeks
d Peter lost 6 kg. 10% of his starting weight is 10% of 90 = 9 kg, so he does not qualify for his money back.

4 a The range of car speeds in the two streets is the same.
b The modal group of car speeds in Judy's street is 20 mph higher than in Nathan's street.

5 a $\frac{3}{4}$
b £15
c Iron and Cook Set
d Microwave
e

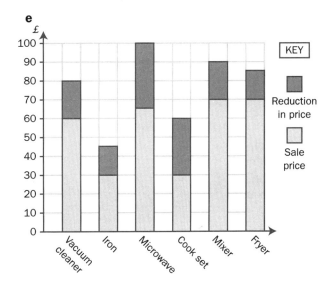

Exercise D6

1 a $\frac{1}{20}$

b $\frac{1}{2}$

c $\frac{1}{4}$

d $\frac{7}{20}$

e $\frac{1}{5}$

2 a 75°

  b i $\frac{1}{4}$

    ii $\frac{1}{3}$

    iii $\frac{5}{24}$

    iv $\frac{5}{24}$

  c 30

3 a 5

  b i $\frac{2}{15}$

    ii $\frac{11}{60}$

    iii $\frac{1}{6}$

    iv $\frac{3}{20}$

    v $\frac{1}{5}$

    vi $\frac{1}{6}$

  c Roll the dice more times.

4 a

	RED				
TOTAL	1	2	3	4	5
1	2	3	4	5	6
2	3	4	5	6	7
3	4	5	6	7	8
4	5	6	7	8	9

(BLUE rows 1–4)

  b 5 or 6

  c $\frac{1}{5}$

5 a April, May

  b Daffodil

  c February

  d Crocus

  e i $\frac{1}{5}$

    ii Number line 0 to 1 with x marked between $\frac{2}{5}$ and $\frac{3}{5}$

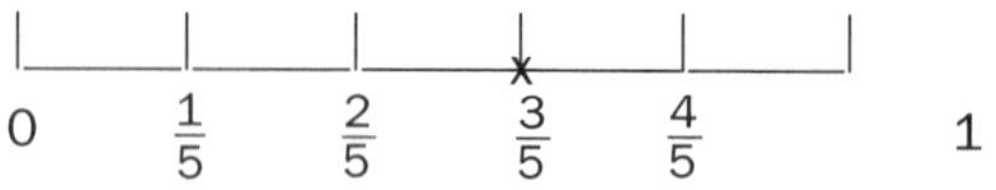

6 0.45

1 a 9
b 24
c 1, 2, 4, 9, 24, 36

2 a 6.9 cm
b
A   B

3 a 383
b 10.24

4 a

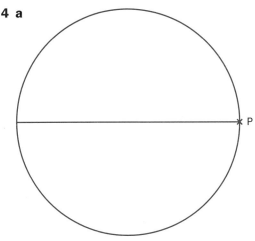

b i chord
ii sector

5 a 6
b 2
c 2.5
d 18

6 a £100

7 a $70 \times 3 = 210$
b $10 \times 3, 6 \times 5$

8 a red-black, red-red, red-white, green-black, green-red, green-white, blue-black, blue-red, blue-white

9 a 152 min
b 2 hrs 32 min

10 a $5^3 = 125$
b $3^4 = 81$

11 £6.60 per kg

12 a 22
b To find the nth term, add n to the previous term.
c 211

13 a 4 °C
b 11 °C
c The temperature appears to have reached a plateau already.

14 a 26 min
b 0841

15 a Area = 12
b M = (3,3)

16 a £120 : £40
b $\frac{1}{10}$

17 a $6x(x^2 + 3)$
b $3(x + 4) - 2(x + 1) = 3x + 12 - 2x - 2 = x + 10$
c $x = 4$

18 $A = \dfrac{\pi D^2}{4} = \dfrac{22}{7} \times \dfrac{12^2}{4} = \dfrac{22}{7} \times 36 = 113.1429$

19 a

x	−1	0	1	2	3
y	4	1	0	1	4

b

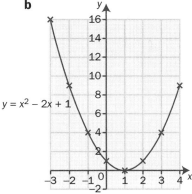

$y = x^2 - 2x + 1$

20 a 122
b i 38 kg
ii 40 kg

21

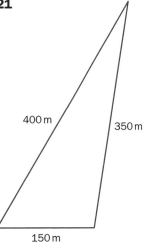

400 m   350 m

150 m

22 a 8.637 467 277
b 8.64

23 a 0.3
b 135 times

24 84

25 2.7%

26 a $x = 4$
b $x = -2$

27 $5.26\dot{6}$

28 109 cm³